LEIF ERIKSSON

LEIF ERIKSSON

FIRST VOYAGER TO AMERICA

KATHERINE B. SHIPPEN

HARPER & BROTHERS, NEW YORK

LEIF ERIKSSON

CONTENTS

THIS is the story of Leif Eriksson, and of how in the spring of the year 1003 he sailed across the western ocean from Greenland, and found a new world.

He left no written record of his discovery, nor did he erect any building that has remained; no sword or shield or helmet has been found to prove that he ever walked on this new shore.

But his own people were so impressed with his exploit that they told of his voyage again and again. In Iceland the skalds sang of it in their sagas. Finally in about 1300 the sagas were written down.

There are a great many Icelandic sagas, but five of them mention Leif Eriksson. The chief source for this story of Leif's life is the Karlsefni Saga.

Because the record is a saga and not a historical document, there are many points about which we cannot be sure. Was Vinland, where Leif landed, the shore of Massachusetts Bay? Or the shore of Long Island Sound? Further north than either of those? Further south? We do not know.

Neither do we know exactly why Leif never returned to Vinland, for the sagas do not say. Did domestic cares keep him at home? Or did he find that the markets of northern Europe provided better business? There is no way of knowing. And it does not greatly matter.

What is important is the fact that Leif Eriksson, without compass and without chart, sailed with his companions across the open ocean, and was the first European to see America. That was nearly five hundred years before Columbus came.

The story begins not with Leif, but with his father, Erik the Red—

LEIF ERIKSSON

1.

THE THOR POST AND
THE ICELAND SHORE

THE fog hung close down over the water. It hid the Iceland coast completely, although Erik calculated that they must be near it. The waves were high in spite of the shroud of mist. The prow of the vessel, grotesquely carved as the head of a gryphon, plunged through one wave after another, and emerged again, dripping. The wadmal sail, striped purple and blue, bellied in the gale. The rowers bent to their oars with a monotonous rhythm. There was no sound save the creak of the ropes, the splash of the oars, the crash of the waves against the gunwales of the ship as it moved forward through the lonely sea.

Erik stood at the bow, his red beard crusted with salt from the flying spray, his sea hat pulled down close over his forehead. All day he had been at the helm, but now he had given over the steering to one of the men, and moved to the bow of the vessel, as if to be nearer to the land he sought.

"Iceland," he was thinking. "We should be there soon. If this fog would only clear we should see the coast by now." He strained his eyes, red with the salt spray, to try to see the faint line that meant that land was near. He could not reach it too quickly: there was so much to do. Houses to be built on a new claim, and barns. Flocks to be started, grass to be stored.

"By next year things ought to be in shape," he was thinking. "I'll go on a trading trip then. England maybe or Ireland. The churchmen may make a fight for their treasures," he thought, fingering his sword. He smiled. "I'd come back rich from a trip like that."

At the stern of the boat Erik's wife Thorhild sat on a pile of chests and boxes, and shivered, and tried to pull her mantle closer around her. The waves kept breaking over the side of the boat: the water was icy cold.

Thorhild was not much more than twenty. And even as she sat there crying, and drenched with sea water, you could see that she was beautiful with her deep blue eyes and rich fair hair. Today there was no color in her face, and dark shadows lay under her eyes, but the face had vitality, like a lamp that would glow again when the flame was lighted. Now and again Thorhild tried to dry her eyes with the corner of her mantle, but it was no use: the mantle was too wet.

Over and over in her mind the events of the last few days repeated themselves. She and Erik had gone to a feast at the house of a neighbor, and Erik had had a brawl with one of the men there. Words had been followed by blows, and then the two men had seized their arms. The women had run up and tried to throw cloths over their weapons, and the men had tried to drag the fighters apart. But it was no use. Finally Erik had cleft the man's skull from the crown down to the chin. Thorhild shivered as she thought of how it bled.

Killing a man meant banishment from Norway. And though she could have remained behind without him, Thorhild had chosen to go with her husband.

"I could have stayed," she kept thinking as the sea came washing over the ship. "I could have stayed at home. But something made me go with him. . . . Now we shall not see the Norway mountains again, nor the pine trees, nor the deep blue fjords. . . ."

Slowly the realization sank deeper and deeper. "We shall not see our house again."

But the sound of her sobbing was lost in the sound of the sea.

Erik, looking into the fog with his back turned toward her, did not see her tears.

The slaves bent to their oars, the waves beat against

the gunwales of the boat, the hours passed: monotony is a part of the life of the sea.

Then the wind changed: sharply, without warning it veered to the south. The fog rolled back. The sun shone. Clear in the sunshine they saw the land before them. The cliffs of western Iceland rose sharply up from the sea: the high plateau was golden in the sun. And as they watched, the rough gray ocean turned blue—a cold, clear, icy blue.

Erik turned to the rowers in excitement. "Rest the oars," he cried. "Land! Land ahead!"

The slaves leaned on their oars, while the ship tossed up and down in the waves. And Erik climbed quickly down the ladder that led to the storage space below the deck.

Soon he appeared again dragging a long carven post. "Help me!" he cried to the slave nearest him. The man left his seat and took hold of the end of the post. They brought it up, bumping and thudding as it came.

The post was a heavy one, carved from a thick tree trunk. The carving was very curiously done, but no one could doubt when he saw it that the image was that of the god Thor. The maker had painted Thor's mantle red, and edged it with a border of gold. In the god's hand he had placed the hammer with which he might perform his godly work. For many years the post had stood before the high seat in Erik's hall in Norway.

"Take care!" Erik said, tipping the god's head up to the edge of the gunwale.

The men rose from their seats, the better to see, and Thorhild ceased her crying in the presence of the god.

"Now lift the feet. Now push." And they pushed, and Thor slid head first into the waves.

The push that Erik and his man had given was so great, that the post went sliding across the water in the direction of the shore. The men watching it saw it disappear as the waves washed over it, and then it appeared again, and drifted on.

"We need not watch it longer," Erik said at last. "Thor will make his own way."

So they took up their oars again, and the ship pushed on toward the bright shore. Just before they reached it Erik unhinged the carved gryphon's head at the ship's prow in order that the spirits on the new shore might not be frightened.

They landed toward evening in a little cove, and moored the ship. From it they brought some tents of dark woven goat's hair, and pitched them on the beach. And soon their fires were lighted though they found only a little driftwood and no other wood of any kind. After they had dried their clothes and eaten, they slept, and the stars were clear over where they lay.

In the morning Erik started to search for the place where the Thor post had been washed ashore. He found it without much difficulty, only a short distance from where they had camped.

"This is the place," Erik said. "Thor has chosen this place for us." And since no one else had claimed that part of the shore, he claimed it. He shot flaming arrows across every stream on his land, and built four strong cairns of stone at the four corners of his claim.

That was in the spring. All through the spring and summer he was busy settling his place. He drew his ship up on the shore and covered it with a coat of pitch, so that it would be ready for future journeys. He traded the goods that he had brought from Norway for a herd of sheep. He built a house with thick walls of sod, and a good thatched roof. And another house beside it to shelter his sheep, and another for his slaves. Soon he was beginning to plan for the spring trading expedition.

His life in Iceland was not so isolated as might have been expected in a frontier community. Sometimes he had his horse saddled, and rode off to a neighbor's to spend an evening in drinking and listening to the songs of some skald. Among his neighbors he was accepted for what he was, nor was he ever asked why he had come to his new settlement.

Often, especially through the winter, when the snow sifted down outside the door, and the darkness closed in through the hours of day as well as night, Erik and his neighbors talked of the voyages they would make when the ice broke up and the water was open for ships again.

So the seasons succeeded one another. In the second spring, Erik's son was born.

2.

"HIS NAME IS LEIF!"

ERIK pushed open the door of the small chamber where the child had been born, and entered. The old midwife, square built and ugly, came toward him and put the child into his arms.

"You have a son," she said.

Erik took the baby to the window and let the light fall on it. He examined its small head covered with soft dark hair, its small red ears. He saw that the body was firm and well shaped, that the arms and legs were strong. The baby stirred as he touched it, and began to cry.

Erik smiled. "It is a fine strong boy. Take it and nourish it," he said to his wife. "We will let it live."

Thorhild, who had been watching from the bed with anxious eyes, smiled too. She put out her arm when Erik gave the baby to her, and gathered it to

8

her breast. Under the soft coverlet of eiderdown she felt warm and safe, knowing that her son's first danger had been averted, that he would not be abandoned to hunger and cold and the prowling animals of the moor: that she would see him grow, and live.

After a while she gave him to the midwife again. "See that he is swaddled tight," she said.

Erik sent word to his friends not many days later, inviting them to come to the naming of his son. They came, in their most brilliant mantles and with shining armor, and rode to Erik's place on little Iceland horses whose flanks were red with mud for the thaws were just beginning.

Most of them had come some distance. Thorstein traveled all the way from his house by the waterfall at Barnafoss. And Herjolf rode down from the plain that lies close under the volcano at Hekla. After them, Gunnar arrived: he owned the biggest flock of sheep in Iceland. And with him was Thorey who lived along the coast north of Erik's place. Bjorn was there too, grayhaired and beaten by the sea; and Bjarni whose ship had pushed further north than any that had ever sailed.

Erik stood at the door of his house to greet them. "*Kom heil!*" he said, as he kissed each man.

They tied their horses to a long fence outside Erik's house and entered, their heavy boots stamping on the earthen floor, their weapons clanking as they moved.

It was warm, and they threw off their mantles, pulled off their corselets, and loosened their shirts at the throat as soon as they came indoors. Then they hung their shields along the wall, and rested their spears in a corner, and seated themselves at the long board of Erik's hall.

Erik himself sat in the high seat at the head of the table. Thorhild had seen that the room was prepared for the occasion although she was not there. New grass had been freshly strewn on the floor: it smelled fragrant and good. Bright-colored cushions had been set on the benches, and wonderfully woven tapestries hung on the wall. The name for Thorhild's baby would be given in no mean place, although his mother could not take part in the ceremony of the naming.

When all were seated, the slaves brought out the casks of ale. And now the drinking horns were passed from hand to hand along the table.

"My son is to be named," Erik said, raising the foaming horn to his lips.

"How will you name him?" Bjarni asked. "Will one name be enough, or will you give him two names, like Gunnlaug Ormstunga or Arinbjorn Hersi? Men with names like those have dignity, are respected by those around them."

But Bjarni's dreams of dignity were lost, for Herjolf interrupted him.

"He ought to have a god's name combined with his name," he said. "If you name him Thorvald or Thorgils, there is no doubt but he will have protection from Thor. A man might need that in days like these."

"Ay, yes," Gunnar said. Gunnar was a skald: he loved the sound of rhyming words. "If you had several sons, you could make their names rhyme, like Lit and Vit."

Old Bjorn said nothing, but passed his horn down the table for more ale. Erik, too, listened in silence.

So they sat around the long board, arguing and talking, until it seemed as if it would be impossible to settle on a name for the baby. But at last, Erik rose in his seat.

"His name will be Leif," he said.

Then at length the baby was brought in, wrapped in its swaddling clothes, and the men around the table raised their drinking horns. "Leif!" they cried and each man took a mighty draught.

Erik emptied his horn first. It was a larger horn than any of the others. He prized it beyond all his possessions, for he had brought it from Norway. It was carved with a design of sea waves and polar bears, and bound with shining silver.

Now as a servant brought the baby to him, he pushed back his chair, and rose to take the child in his arms. Then from his great horn which a slave had filled with water, very carefully he dropped water on the baby's head, as rain might fall upon its head from the clouds.

"His name is Leif!" he cried in a resounding voice.

It was as if he meant not only the men in the hall to hear him, but all the universe outside. "His name is Leif!" he cried again.

Then the men around the table rose, lifting their horns high, and drinking deep. "Leif!" they shouted till their strong voices shook the rafters. "Leif!"

But the ritual was not over: the ceremony was not done. For in his belt Erik carried a hammer. Its head was fashioned from Iceland basalt and polished till it gleamed. Its strong straight haft was of Norway pine. Drawing this hammer from his belt, he lifted it above his head.

"Come, Thor," he said, "to help this child. Help him with the strength of your hammer. Guard him from cold and fire. Guide his ship across the water, wherever he may sail." He struck the table a sharp blow with the hammer. "Bring him good fortune! Be his friend!"

There was a silence in the room. No man spoke or moved: the air seemed heavy round them.

Then those who were near the door saw a jagged fork of lightning cleave the sky. And immediately a deep rumble of thunder filled the room, and there was a sound of rain falling hard on the thatched roof, and beating down hard on the earth outside the door.

"So Thor has heard!" someone said. And Erik and the others were content, though the baby cried at the top of his lungs as if he was indignant.

"The boy will be lucky," they said to one another

later as they took down their shields and went out-
doors to untie their horses. "Never has Thor spoken
more clearly. Erik has been fortunate in naming his
son." And they climbed to their saddles and started
down the road.

Erik stood in his doorway leaning on his sword,
watching his departing guests. The rain had cleared
abruptly as it had come. The puddles in the ruts were
shining in the sun.

"*Far Heil!*" he called as he watched them trotting
off across the moor. The sun was warm, shining down
on his red hair and beard, his weather-beaten face,
and the soft folds of his blue mantle.

And to himself he thought, "I have a son, Leif—
a son to help me man my galleys, to sail the oceans
of the world, and trade, and fight—a son!"

So Erik turned and entered his hall again. The
spring sun was still high in the sky, though it was
past ten o'clock at night.

3.

A BOY LEARNS
WHAT HE MUST

NO Viking in those days thought it proper to rear his own son, so Leif was sent to live with a foster father when he was eight years old. Erik chose Thyrker to educate his son.

Thyrker was short, homely, good-natured and very wise,—or so it seemed to Leif. He came from Germany where he had fallen captive to Erik in a marauding expedition. But though Erik brought him back to Iceland in his galley, he had not enslaved him. Thyrker married, and had a son of his own, but whenever his lively blue eyes were set on Erik, there was a light of kindliness in them, for he knew he owed him his freedom.

"You'll have Thyrker's boy Konrad to play with,"

Erik told Leif as they rode across the moor to Thyrker's house. "He's younger than you are of course, and not so strong, but he'll keep you from feeling lonely." And afterwards he said, "I hope Thyrker will teach you the Celtic tongue, and maybe Russian. When you are a man and go trading it will be a help if you can speak to people in their own languages."

Leif soon found that the new languages whose words were so difficult to say, were only the beginning of the things he was to learn. For one thing he had to learn to read the runes. In the long winter when Leif was nine years old, after Konrad had been put to bed, he and Thyrker sat close to the fire, while the snow drifted deep outside the door and the wind came crying across the moor from the north, and Leif learned to read the runes. He learned them first by picking out the characters engraved on Thyrker's sword, and then he read others that Thyrker made with a bit of charcoal from the fire, writing on a smooth piece of stone. By the time spring came he could read the engraving on a flat stone that told how Thorgund had been lost on a trading expedition in the far north. He read many other inscriptions after that.

Later Thyrker taught him the ways of trade: how many fox pelts in exchange for a gold armlet: how much timber for a strong male slave.

"Sometimes you can take gold in exchange for the things you want," Thyrker explained. "If you have the gold drawn into long spiral wires, it's easy to measure the exact amount. . . . Some countries make their gold into coins. . . ."

Then he would go to his cupboard, and bring from it a leather bag, heavy with coins. And they would pore over the curious metal pieces, examining the designs carved on them—the heads of kings and potentates, the words written in strange languages.

"These I got in Germany," Thyrker would say, holding up several pieces of gold. "I took a load of furs to trade—beautiful furs they were. The animals had been trapped high up on the side of a mountain. . . . They paid me well. . . . Many of the coins I squandered, but I kept these." He let them chink together in his rough hand.

"And these coins came from Russia," he went on, as he chose several from the heap to show the boy. "Well I remember those people. They drink vodka and not ale, and when you sit down to eat with them, the table is loaded with more food than you could eat in a week—" The old eyes sparkled at the memory of those feasts.

"If you ever sail to Russia," he told the boy, "go in the spring. The northern ocean freezes early in the winter and unless you choose to stay a year, as many do, you'll not get back unless you start in the spring. I remember once when I went—"

So on and on old Thyrker talked, and Leif, listening, wondered when he himself would sail a serpent ship, when he would go on trading expeditions, and what brave deeds he would perform. And he was restless to grow up.

Sometimes Thyrker taught him to recite old sagas. First the old man said the words, and Leif repeated them. Then the boy said them by himself, and his master grunted approval. He learned tales of battles and of great voyages on stormy seas, and tales of women with thick fair hair and beautiful garments. The women that Leif saw in Iceland were not like these. The men in the sagas were quick with their swords, strong and eager for action. Saying the sagas over filled the boy with boldness and a restlessness to see new things.

But if Leif liked saying the sagas better than anything else, Thyrker, being German, liked to study plants. When they walked across the moor he stopped to examine every leaf and stem and flower that grew along the way, and talked continually about how different these were from the plants in Germany. "Not half so beautiful," he kept saying, remembering the violets and wild roses he had known in his youth.

"These are not half so beautiful. . . . Look at this little plant though. See how it grows there on the rock with hardly any earth to feed it."

Leif looked, and thought the little bright colored Iceland flowers gay enough, and wondered what the flowers were like in the land that Thyrker knew.

Sometimes the old man bored him, with all his information: yet he learned what Thyrker taught him as a matter of course, and kept the facts in his mind: they might be of some use to him later.

There were plenty of things Leif learned without being taught. Sometimes he rode races with the other boys who lived nearby, gripping his little brown colt hard between his knees. Sometimes his filly put her head down and flung her hind legs up into the air, and Leif hung on delightedly, until she went racing on, while Thyrker watched from his doorway.

Often on sunny days he used to lie in the sulphur pools that were not hard to find near Thyrker's house, feeling the warmth of the water steal through his strong young body, closing his eyes with the warm sun touching his eyelids.

And again he swam in the sparkling water of the harbor. Then when he saw a galley coming, he swam to it and pulled himself up over the gunwale, to show the men aboard how he could run from one oar blade to another as the great ship rowed across the water, and how he could leap from the last oar into the boat again. The oarsmen used to laugh to see him do it— "Do it again! Do it again!" they used to cry.

When he was old enough Leif learned to use a sword, a broadax and a spear. "Let me use *your* sword," he used to say to Thyrker, and his master, smiling to see how the boy enjoyed the beauty of the blade, readily agreed. It was a lovely weapon. Its hilt was carved with a design of dolphins, and it was inlaid with gold. The slender blade of blue-black steel flashed through the air, thin and deadly as a flash of lightning. Leif used to dream of the day when he himself would own a sword like that.

But of all the excitements of those quick passing days, nothing ever seemed to Leif quite so exciting or so beautiful as the sight of ships when they came back into the harbor from distant seas. He and his friends watched them often, and always there was a little shiver of joy in Leif when he saw them. Sometimes one or two arrived, sometimes as many as twenty, their bright sails set, their oars cutting the water with rhythmic sweeps. There was nothing in the world so grand to see, Leif thought.

Generally the ships stopped when they were still some distance from the shore, while the polished shields were hung along the gunwales in a shining row. After the shields had been set in place, the men took up their oars again, rowing in perfect form with long graceful strokes. As they approached the shore the people saw the carved prows of the vessel flashing with bright paint and gilt, and they set up a shout of welcome as one after another the bows were pushed up on the sandy beach.

Then there was always a babel of excitement as the men jumped from the boats waist deep into the water and came striding ashore. After the boats had been made fast, the people followed the voyagers to some nearby house where they might fill their drinking horns with ale, and tell of their journeys, and show the special treasures they had brought home with them while the cargo was being unloaded from the ships.

Leif was always there when the ships landed. People said that no Viking ever made the harbor that Leif was not standing on the shore to greet him, to hear where he had been.

4.

NEWS OF A LAND
TO THE WEST

ONCE, it was in the long days of midsummer, Leif was standing on a bluff near the ocean, when he saw a speck of a ship just at the horizon's edge. It was a bright, windy day. The smell of thyme rose from the ground at his feet, and the moor was covered with the small bright flowers of the saxifragia. But these things were of no interest to Leif. His eyes looked out to where the white-fringed waves were racing, and there at the very rim of the ocean he saw a ship.

He shaded his eyes with his hands and looked again. The air was very clear: he could see for a great distance. There was no doubt of it—it was a ship.

Leif sat down on a stone to watch. The gulls

wheeled and dipped over his head, the waves churned against the shore below him. The smell of the sea and the smell of the thyme mingled together till the air was filled with them. And the ship came nearer.

Now Leif could see that the sail of the approaching ship was battered and faded, and that the men rowed slowly as if they were very tired. They did not stop off shore to display their shields. Steady but slow, they came into the harbor. When they were quite near Leif could see that the side of the ship had a big patch in it, as if a hole had been rammed into the planks. The carven prow was dull and battered: it must have been buffetted by cruel seas.

"It's Bjarni!" Leif thought, running toward the shore. "It's Bjarni back again!"

It was a year since Bjarni had sailed. Leif remembered that other summer day. The boat was freshly painted then with gleaming black. The sail was new, the rowers fresh and strong. Bjarni had set off for Greenland, carrying a valuable cargo of timber and gifts for his parents who had gone there to live. No one had heard of him since then: no one knew what had become of him. It was well known that the voyage was a long one, and Greenland was a rugged country —nevertheless vessels did make that journey every year and made a safe return. But no one knew what had become of Bjarni—had some misfortune come to him?

And now, "It's Bjarni!" Leif called out, running

toward the beach where the weary vessel was nosing
up on the shore.

He saw the rowers ship their oars and leave the
boat. He saw Bjarni, the ship's owner, climb ashore.
His face was thinner than he remembered and cut
with deep lines—runes that Leif could not read.

"Bjarni?" he said, walking along beside him. And
Bjarni remembered him and smiled.

Back in the hall where Bjarni and his friends gathered Leif sat at the edge of the little group.

"Did you reach Greenland?" one of them asked.
And Bjarni shook his head.

"We took our course steering by the North Star,"
Bjarni said. "But after we had sailed a long time, the
mists came down and there were no stars to sail by,
and no sun. We tried to keep our bearings by the
wind, but the wind changed and changed again, and
we had no way of knowing where we were."

"After we had gone six days the mists cleared. We
knew we should have reached Greenland.... But there
was no land there ..."

The room was quiet. Leif moved closer to Bjarni,
studying his face.

"So we kept on," Bjarni said at last. "We rowed
through the northern sea. And soon we saw on every
side the gleaming forms of icebergs. We hardly dared
to move at all for fear of them.... Give me more ale.

"We hit an iceberg—the water came pouring into
the ship. We patched the hole with some pieces of the

deck and kept on, not knowing when we would strike
another, or when our vessel would be locked in the ice.

"We were not afraid to die: what must be must be."
Bjarni looked at the faces round him as if he thought
they might be scornful of his fears. "Every man must
meet his death some time," he said. "But to sink into
that icy water—and no man knowing what had become of us—

"Now we began to wonder how long our food would
last, and to measure the water in the casks.

"And then the fog came down around us again.
It settled round us so close, the men on the ship could
hardly see each other. We could not see the color of the
sea—we could not see the sea at all.

"But out of the fog a faint steady wind blew. We
sailed with that wind: we had no way of knowing from
what quarter it came. Day and night, day and night,
and no sun or moon or stars, and the same faint wind
blowing behind us. After we had gone four days I
gave orders to strike sail and wait for the fog to clear.

"The fog did clear, that very night. A strong wind
came tearing out of the east. We hoisted sail again,
and gave our vessel to it. The ship flew across the
water. It flew like a harpoon when it leaves the
hunter's hands, and the white wake went streaming
out behind us. Just after sunrise the second day,
we saw land.

" 'We can see Greenland now,' I thought, and I
shouted to the helmsman to keep on the course.

"But we knew that the Greenland coast had tall headlands that are white with glaciers, and there were no glaciers here. The shores of this land were green. The forest came right down to the edge of the water. And there were no mountains, only row after row of wooded hills. . . . We had no idea where we were.*

"The sailors wanted to land, explore the hills, get an additional load of timber maybe," Bjarni continued. "But a good steady wind was blowing. So I said, 'We can come back later.' I didn't want to steer close to the land for fear we might hit a rock and be wrecked. You have to be careful—"

"Didn't you land at all?" someone asked him.

"We went on," Bjarni said. "I told them to let out the sheet and sail before the wind.

"We sailed for two days and a night, and once again we came to land. But this land was flat, and forest covered, and the glaciers of Greenland were not there. But the wind still held."

"Didn't you land there either?" an old man near the doorway asked him.

"I had a valuable cargo to deliver," Bjarni said. "I wanted to see my parents in Greenland—and the wind held. We sailed on and on, but the course must have been set too far south. . . . We never saw Greenland at all—"

*The lands Bjarni saw are thought to have been Newfoundland and Labrador.

That night in his bed at Thyrker's house, Leif lay awake, thinking of Bjarni's voyage.

"He came to land," he said to himself in the dark. "A new strange land that men had never heard of, in the western seas. . . . If I could go there I would climb those cliffs to see what it was like. . . ."

So he pulled his bearskin closer round him, and pushed his face down into the warm fur, dreaming of the strange headlands in that unknown place.

"And Bjarni never even set his foot on that land," he kept thinking. And then he slept.

5.

AN AX AND A
BUNCH OF ARROWS

So the years passed, and Leif was twelve, and people said he was a man now, ready to return to his father's house. On his twelfth birthday Thyrker went out to watch while he mounted his horse to start for home.

"I'll never forget you, Thyrker," Leif said. "Wherever I go, I'll want you to be there."

Thyrker smiled. "Keep practicing the runes," he called. "Keep practicing—" And Leif, not even seeing that the old man was sad, but thinking only that he himself was a man grown now, put spurs to his little horse, waved to old Thyrker standing in the road, and galloped toward his father's house.

Erik's place had grown much richer and more impressive since he left it. The herds had multiplied.

Erik had built new houses, and bought new slaves to work for him, and Thorhild had borne him two more sons. Leif, coming home now, was welcomed as his father's heir.

"A fine strong youth," Erik's neighbors were soon saying. "Able to hold his own in a wrestling match —sharp in a bargain. Will you take him with you to Ireland in the spring?"

And Erik was filled with pride, feeling that his son was like himself, but stronger, and he began to make plans for a great expedition to Ireland with a dozen trading ships, and himself and Leif in the biggest and most beautiful of them.

But the voyage to Ireland was not taken in the spring.

It was early in the morning a few days after his homecoming. Leif had only just risen, and was pouring water into a basin to wash himself, when he heard strange hoofbeats on the road outside.

He threw the door open in time to meet the messenger who was reining in his horse.

"The Assembly meets on Odin's day at the Thingvellir!" the messenger cried, and he handed Leif a small ax with a sheaf of arrows tied around it.

"Take these on to the next house and give them the summons," the messenger said. And as Leif stood there holding the ax and arrows in his hand, the messenger turned his horse's head and rode away.

Erik appeared at the door just then.

"I thought the summons would come soon," he said. "Be careful not to drop the arrows: it is a capital offense to let them touch the ground." And then he said, "We'll ride over with them to Thorgund's at once. Tomorrow we can start for Thingvellir."

Leif handed the arrows to his father, feeling somehow as he did so, that he had grown taller and much older, now that he was going to the Iceland Assembly.

Leif's father was in fine spirits as they prepared for the journey. "You'll see," he said to the boy, pulling on his mail corselet and fastening his knife in his belt. "Everyone will be there. There's nothing like the Iceland Parliament: no place in the world where justice is done so well. And there's plenty to be done there besides just talk. It's the greatest time of the year."

Leif felt a quiver of excitement. He pulled his metal helmet down on his head. The headpiece was decorated with two eagle's wings: he had shot the eagle himself.

"It's better to be armed," his father had said. "You never know—"

He did not finish the sentence, but Leif knew what he meant. They might meet Thorgest.

The feud between Erik and Thorgest had started when Leif was still only two or three years old. Thorgest was a rich merchant who had a large estate across the moor. One spring when Erik was going on a long trading expedition to the Mediterranean, he had taken several of his most treasured possessions and given them to Thorgest for safe-keeping.

"They will be less likely to be stolen while I am away if you keep them," he had said. And Thorgest had laughed, and said there was plenty of room in his house for them. Among the treasures Erik brought were his beautiful carved drinking horn, and the Thor post that he had brought from the home of his ancestors in Norway.

After several months when Erik came back to claim his possessions, Thorgest offered to pay him a good price for the Thor post. He thought it old fashioned, but had none of his own, and it would give a certain distinction to his hall.

"It is not for sale," Erik had said shortly. And he had attempted to enter the hall and take it for himself.

But Thorgest put out his foot and tripped Erik as he was stepping over the threshold. A bloody fight had followed, the noise of it brought men and women running to tear the two men apart.

It was well known that a bitter feud had started then. Each man had sworn before witnesses that he would not go in search of the other, but if he ever chanced to meet him, he would fight him to the death.

"He won't show his face," Leif said to his father, lacing up his high leather boot. He considered Thorgest a coward.

They started early for the Thingvellir, riding

along on small dappled horses whose coats had been brushed until they glistened, and whose manes and tails shone in the sun like yellow silk. Under their brightly painted wooden saddles, their soft wool saddle blankets were striped red and white. Their bridles were decorated with silver, and each horse had a silver bit intricately carved.

Close behind Erik and Leif rode a retinue of servants. Erik did not say whether he took them because they would be useful, or because he wanted to impress his friends. Some of his slaves were on horseback, and some rode in a large open cart packed in with casks of ale, barrels of food, and furniture.

They took the road toward the west, trotting along over a high plateau. The wind was blowing in from the ocean in gusts that morning: the heads of the small bright flowers bent over when the wind came, and then stood up again, quivering. The air was clear and fresh with a smell of salt and heather, and the sea birds wheeled and dipped in the sky.

As they went on other people joined them. There were women as well as men, for many took their wives with them to the Assembly. Thorhild, however, had preferred to remain at home with the younger children, so Leif and Erik shared each other's company.

The crowd along the road grew thicker and thicker as they went. Some of the travelers had come great distances across plains and deserts. Others had climbed through mountain passes, or forded rushing streams, or trotted over high plateaus. Almost all of them were on horseback, although a few walked, with staffs in their hands and packs on their shoulders.

Soon they were joined by jugglers and acrobats, by men who led dancing bears with chains fastened to rings in their noses, by beggars and fortunetellers, and all the riff-raff who might be expected when a great congregation of people come together.

The road began to climb now, and the horses and the people moved more slowly. They climbed up through high passes in the mountains, and finally reached a wide plain which stretched out for some distance before the meeting place. Here Leif and his father dismounted. The slaves got down from the cart and the horses were hitched to posts, while the unpacking started, and father and son began to look around.

It was a curious place. A series of booths had been built around a wide open space. The booths were solidly built of clay brick and provided with shutters and doors, but their rafters were open to the sky.

"This is ours," Erik said. "We'll have the thatch cut in the meadow over there, and soon the roof will be solid as it was last year."

So the order was given, and Erik's slaves set to work. And soon the booth was securely roofed, chairs and plank tables were brought in from the cart, Erik's seat was placed at one end of the table, and a seat for Leif at the other, and the casks of ale were rolled in.

It would be twenty-four hours before the Assembly began, but the booths around the square were already alive with activity. People were greeting each other who had not met for a year. Merchants were bartering: there was a brisk business in horse-trading. In the booth next to theirs, an old friend was arranging a marriage contract for his daughter. "Beautiful she is, fair skinned—worthy to be a prince's wife. . . ."

Leif did not listen, nor was he interested. What did a marriage contract mean to him? There was to be a wrestling match in the square.

After the wrestling match was over, Leif found a fortuneteller. "You will be fortunate," the woman said. "Give me a coin . . . I will tell you more. . . . You will go on great journeys, across wide oceans: it is written here in your hand. Give me a coin—" Leif lingered, marveling, believing. Of course he would go on great voyages: that was the Viking life. He gave more coins—

After he left the fortuneteller he saw that a crowd of people were beginning to congregate. They came pouring into the square, singing, clapping their hands, and a dance began. Leif joined them, for he loved to dance.

They formed a great revolving circle, and soon the circle became three circles, one inside the other: then the three circles broke into hundreds of whirling couples, until the whole square rocked with the rhythm of dancing feet. Old people and young people, men and women, boys and girls—all danced together. Leif saw that his own father was one of them. Erik danced on and on with his long beard flying, and Leif paid little heed, for he was reeling with the intoxication of the motion.

Then, suddenly as it had started, the dance died down, like a fire that has spent itself. Darkness began to gather in the square. People were kindling pine knots, and hanging them on brackets outside their doors. Somewhere a skald began to sing: Leif heard the strings of his harp rippling through the dusk.

As he listened, another sound cut across the music. Slowly across the square a man moved with a long horn at his lips. "The Thing Peace has been proclaimed," he cried. The horn made his voice echo and re-echo among the booths.

6.

THE THING PEACE IS BROKEN

THE people began moving toward the temple. The priest, his flowing robes of scarlet and his silvery beard half lighted in the dusk, led the procession. Leif and his father walked with the others.

They mounted the low steps that led up to the sanctuary and entered through the heavily studded doors.

Inside, the room was low and oval. Leif standing beside his father examined it with a lively interest, for he had never seen such a great rich temple before. Before him the wooden altar was covered with a sheet of metal, and on it he could see the priest's armband, sacred for administering oaths, the great bowl of burnished copper which held the blood of the sacrificial animals, the altar fire.

Behind the altar in a semicircle he saw the wooden
figures of the gods: Thor in the center, taller than the
rest, and at Thor's right and left, Frig and Freya,
Baldur and Odin. They had been clothed in new
garments, rich and beautiful Leif thought them. Red
and purple, blue and yellow—the soft folds of their
mantles seemed to glow and shimmer in the half-light.

Now as Leif watched, a priest laid small sticks on
the fire, then larger ones, and the flames leaped up,
making light where there had been shadows before.
Around the altar the people stood well back, but the
light moved across the intervening space, so that their
faces were lighted up and then veiled in darkness
again. And in the moving light the wooden images of
the gods seemed ugly but alive, with the fire's blazing
and dying.

Soon the fire seemed to take a stronger hold, and all
the room was filled with light. Then the people stood
silent in the presence of the gods.

It was now that the priest threw himself to the
ground and with his forehead touching the tiles of the
floor began to chant. His voice was quiet at first, as
the fire had been, then it grew stronger and stronger,
until it vibrated in every corner of the quiet room.

"O Thor, who art a friend of men," the priest was
crying, "O Odin, Father of us all, and Baldur, thou
gentle one who lovest peace—be here among us now,
and help us—

"See we bring you gifts—"

He waved a hand, and two men approached the altar bearing between them a small white lamb.

The lamb stood on the altar, blinking in the light of the fire.

"We bring a horse—best of the Iceland breed." A small brown and white horse, carefully groomed, was led up to the altar.

"We bring the prow of a ship, that can slip across the waves fast as a moving serpent. . . . These are for you. . . . The best we have."

The priest's high voice went crooning on, and Leif was moved, feeling the presence of the gods.

"Tomorrow, when the great Assembly meets," the priest went on, "when all the men of Iceland come together to do justice—O Thor and Odin: O Baldur, Frig and Freya—be with us then."

The priest's voice died away: the sacrifice was over. Here and there people began moving toward the various gods to make special petitions. Leif standing beside Erik saw his father's eyes move up toward the image of Thor.

"Come on, father," he said, pulling his father by the sleeve. "The people are leaving now . . ." And Erik turned and walked with Leif down the great steps.

It was almost dark in the square now, but guards were holding flaming torches of pine knots, and the moon was rising.

"Lay your weapons and your armor there," cried

the guards, pointing toward a place in the center of the square. "No one may wear armor now: no one may carry a weapon till the Assembly is over. The Thing Peace will be observed."

People were going to the spot the guards indicated, taking off their helmets and their coats of mail, laying down their shields and spears.

"Come back to claim them later," the guards were calling.

Leif and his father followed the others. Leif put his things down first.

"You put your arms on top of mine," he said to his father. And his father also laid down his spear and shield on top of the growing heap.

Just as he put his helmet down a man whom Leif had never seen before came up. He flung his coat of linked mail on the heap, and as he did so jostled Erik.

"Give room," he said.

"Who speaks to me with words like those?" cried Erik.

"I," said the stranger. And he gave Erik a blow that sent him staggering.

Now in the moonlight Erik drew back and looked at the stranger.

"Thorgest!" he said with a quick soft breath. And Leif came close to see the man.

But that word "Thorgest!" and those looks, were only the work of a moment. For Thorgest and Erik were upon each other. Back and forth on the moonlit field they fought. Now the stranger was on top of

Erik, pinning him down. Now Erik had slid out and
gained a hold around his adversary's neck. Now they
were rolling.

Fascinated, Leif watched his father. He himself
had often wrestled. He loved to feel the play and give
of muscles in his arms and legs and back and neck as
he rolled and plunged and kicked: but this was different. His father had met Thorgest. This he knew
was a fight to the death.

A circle of people had gathered now in the moonlight, around the heap of weapons, around the struggling men.

Now and again the fighters broke apart, and then
they were at each other again. No one spoke, no one
interfered, there was only the sound of hard breath-
ing, and the dull thud of heavy fists against flesh. The
people watching knew this was a blood feud: this fight
was in the hands of the gods.

Finally the struggling couple rolled close to the
heap of weapons. And Thorgest managed to free one
arm and reach out for a dagger. He was just about to
lift it for a blow, when Erik too reached for a weapon.
He seized a short-handled battle ax, escaped from
Thorgest's grasp, rose to his knees, and struck. The
force of the blow on Thorgest's head was so great that
the ax was buried deep in his skull.

He crumpled, and lay motionless on the ground. In
the moonlight you could see the dark stain of the blood
growing bigger—

Leif ran to his father, to steady him.

7.

THE TRIAL AND
THE SENTENCE

"THEY'VE bound the thongs too tight," Leif was thinking. "They'll bruise his arms. . . . They had no right to bind them so tight."

But he said nothing, for he knew he could not loosen them. He was walking beside his father in the long procession that made its way to the Hill of Laws, where the Iceland Assembly was to meet.

At another time Leif would have looked at this ancient meeting place with awe—its level plain with the tiers of seats banked round it; its semicircle of mountains on the north, west, and south—gold in the early light and shadowed with purple; its superb view of the deep blue ocean on the east. It was a place where the Iceland people had come every year since

time immemorial to do justice, and there was not a
citizen who was not stirred by the dignity and beauty
of the place. But Leif hardly noticed it at all that
morning, and the people around him might as well
have been a league away. He was conscious of nothing
but his father, walking beside him in silence, his arms
bound tight to his sides with leather thongs, and of
the guards who surrounded him.

They had waited all night for the Assembly. When
the first ray of the sun pierced through a cleft in the
mountains the Law Man who had been watching for
this sign, struck a great bronze gong. This was the
signal that the day had come: the day on which the
great Iceland Assembly was to meet. Then the people, led by an official, walked in procession to the meeting place on the Hill of Laws: Leif and his father
were with them.

They had expected this day to be different. As they
walked along, Leif's mind went back to the morning
only three days before when he had been waked by the
messenger and had opened the door to receive the summons. His father had been in a frenzy of excitement
about the preparations for starting. He had immediately set his servants to work at polishing their armor
and grooming their horses. Everything must be done
quickly. They must start early to give themselves
plenty of time. For the Iceland Assembly was a great
occasion, and this year Erik would bring his son to it.

The guards led them to a bench a little apart from

the others. Erik was permitted to take his seat: Leif
sat beside him.

Now the people around them were settling in their
places. Could it be only three days since he and his
father had started, Leif was wondering, only three
days since they had come trotting along that road with
all the crowds and crowds of people? He remembered how Erik had smiled and laughed with the
friends he met, and pointed Leif out to them. "My
boy," he had heard him saying twenty times. "Almost
as tall as I am now!"

Now Erik sat beside him motionless, and Leif did
not know what he was thinking. His head was bowed
over, his red beard lay on his chest. And the Assembly
that they had looked forward to joining, was trying
Erik for having killed a man.

Leif saw the men of the jury separate themselves
from the other members and take their seats on the
long beach in the center of the amphitheater. The
Law Man made a count of each man as he passed.

"Forty-eight!" he called at last. "The jury is complete!"

The forty-eight on whose judgment his father's
fate depended, were men not unlike his father and
himself. One was an old man with a gray beard, handsomely dressed in a long blue tunic. Another was a
square-built fellow, his yellow hair bleached by the
sun, his face tanned and weathered by many sea
voyages until it was the texture of fine leather. And
one had a heavy purse fastened to his belt, and a fine

gold chain around his neck. Leif studied them, one after another, wondering what manner of men they were. What would they think of his father's act? Was there any kindness in them? Or only hard justice?

And the men of the jury looked across at Erik, with his son sitting beside him. According to the lots that had been cast, their case was to be tried first.

Erik had killed a man: of that there was no doubt. It was their business to decide what his punishment should be.

"Let the witnesses be sworn!" the Law Man cried. And he pulled off a wide gold band that he wore on his left arm and held it out before him. The early sun caught the shine of it and made it blaze like a small fire in his hand.

Now one after another the four witnesses approached and, laying a hand on the glittering gold band, swore by Odin and Thor that they would tell the truth. Then the Law Man put the bracelet back on his arm, and the trial began.

It was not a long trial, for the facts were simple. All agreed that Erik had killed Thorgest, and since there was a feud, everyone there thought him justified. But the fight had occurred after the Thing Peace was announced, after the sacrifices had been made to the gods, after the order had been given to lay all arms aside. Herein lay the serious offense. According to the ancient laws of Iceland, the breaking of the Thing Peace must be punished.

As the morning sun rose higher, its gold light

shone down on the brightly clad people, who sat to consider Erik's crime. Among the people seated around the amphitheater, now one and now another rose and spoke, giving his opinion. Finally when the opinions had been heard, the forty-eight men of the jury withdrew to deliberate. Leif sat quiet, waiting: Erik did not move.

Then the jury came back to their seats, the leader spoke to the Law Man, and a silence hung over the assembly. Was Erik to die for what he had done?

The Law Man rose. Leif saw the long white folds of his robe stir as a slight breeze touched them. He saw the bracelet on his arm shine in the sun. He spoke:

"According to the ancient laws of Iceland, a crime has been committed. The Thing Peace has been broken, the penalty must be paid.

"I who have learned the laws of Iceland from my father, who learned them from his father before him, and before that for many generations, pronounce the law of Iceland.

"Erik who has killed Thorgest, shall be banished from Iceland for three years' time."

Leif saw his father stir a little, but he made no sound.

"His houses, his flocks, and all that he has, shall become the property of the people. He shall be permitted to hold one ship only, with slaves to man it, and livestock enough only to start new herds.

"He shall be given three days in which to depart

from Iceland. After that, any man giving him shelter shall be breaking the law—"

The Law Man stopped. The sentence had been pronounced. The jury turned its attention to another case.

8.

GREENLAND, THE NEW FRONTIER

ERIK and Leif rode back from the Assembly in almost complete silence, their horses keeping pace side by side along the road, the slaves following after in the cart. When they had come almost within sight of home, Leif spoke:

"Could we go back to Norway?" he asked.

"No," Erik answered. "Not to Norway."

And they rode on in silence again.

At last Erik said, "We could go west, to Greenland." Leif did not answer. "It's a rough frontier country," Erik said after awhile. "Now and again sailors have stopped there. . . . They say it's a bleak, rocky coast, but in one part there is grass enough for the herds. We could go there for three years. Perhaps we could make something of it."

Leif said, "Yes, we could go there." And all the
time he was thinking: "That's the place Bjarni was
trying to reach when he got off the course and took
that long voyage. I saw it once. I climbed to the top
of the Detterfoss, and all the time the fog was hanging over the ocean. But as I stood there the fog
parted. And I saw a land, very faint and far away,
before the mists closed down again. . . . What would it
be like there, I wonder . . . a new land. . ."

But he said to his father, "It wouldn't be a long
voyage." And Erik said, "We'll have to tell your
mother."

Thorhild had changed since she had come to Iceland. She had come in tears, weeping for her home in
Norway, afraid of the strange ways of a new country.
Now she was the manager of a large important
household, with many Irish and German slaves to do
her bidding. She had three sons now, and she was
proud that her husband had raised himself to a position of importance among his neighbors. Superintend-
ing the weaving and sewing of the family's clothes,
the cheese- and butter-making, the ale-brewing and
the cooking, she felt herself important and competent
as she walked about their houses, her long yellow
braids lying over her shoulders, her dress hanging in
rich folds over her strong body.

"There will be a great deal to do in three days," she
said. "And there are not even three days left now."
And Erik knew that already she was calculating in

her mind what things she would take with her, and what she would leave.

"The dragon ship will hold more than any of the others," Erik said. "We'll take the dragon ship." He spoke of his largest vessel, a clinker-built ship half-decked over, with a beautiful prow carved like a dragon's head.

"There will be room for thirty slaves to row it, and some of the freedmen from the place will probably come with their families. I think that Thyrker will want to come. We'll need hands in a place like that. We can take about fifty on her besides the livestock and the fodder."

Thorhild said, "We'll take the big loom, and the butter churn, and the ale casks—and food to eat on the way. Who knows what we shall find in a place like that?"

Her voice conveyed the feeling that whatever she found she would cope with.

Leif listened to their planning, and helped with the preparations, half dreaming. "A new land toward the west," he kept thinking. "What would it be like? What other lands were there beyond that? Would he ever see them? If he could sail on beyond the place where they would settle, on to the land Bjarni had seen, he would not pass by it, unvisited, as Bjarni had done. He would climb up on that shore and see what it was like."

"Everything's ready," his father was saying.

So the ship cast off from the shore, the square sail bellied in a fair wind, and the rhythmic oars flashed in the sun. And Leif stood beside Erik at the prow, while Thorhild sat comfortably on a pile of furs at the stern and the two younger children played with knucklebones on the deck. Below decks there was an occasional bleat or grunt from some sheep or pig, while over them all the smells of straw and dried fish and animals were blended together, not dissipated by the following wind.

Late in the afternoon the rowers stopped, the sail was lowered, and the vessel rolled in the trough of the waves. Then a small fire was built on some flat stones on the deck, hot porridge was made in a great kettle, and cups of ale passed round. In an hour's time they were on their way again.

If they were outlaws, it did not matter to Leif. Everything was comfortable, well-organized, and orderly. His father had killed a man, but it was a man with whom he had had a feud, so no one could blame him. The strain of the trial on the Hill of Laws was forgotten now. They were on their way to a new land.

As night fell, the fog settled down around their boat, but they kept on. Erik consulted no one, spoke to no one in fact. He merely ordered that they keep the same direction. By morning, it was understood, they should be within sight of land.

No one on board slept that night. They sat in the dark, with no light save the slight gleam of some

embers of the cooking fire on the deck, while the
ship moved across the water to the creak and splash
of its oars.

The light came gradually, making the forms of sail,
oars and rowers take on shape. When it was day, they
saw that the fog had rolled away, and looking toward
the west, they saw the outline of a rocky coast.

The mountains along that coast were bleak and
rugged and many of their peaks were covered with
snow as if someone had flown over them dropping
enormous handkerchiefs. The men on the boat stared
at them curiously as every traveler stares at an approaching land. Soon they began making preparations to go ashore, for the mountains seemed so near
that there was no doubt that they would reach them
in a few hours.

When they came closer, however, they saw that they
could not land, for between them and the shore the
surface of the sea was covered with a deep crust of
ice so thick and strong that try as they might they
could not force their vessel through it. The ice lay in
great irregular cakes, level and close together. Between them here and there were small blue pools and
cracks of sea water, and the tracery of these cracks
and pools was constantly changing as the pack moved.

They looked at the ice floe curiously, for such a
thing had never been seen off the coast of Iceland,
though sailors voyaging north had told of it. The people on board the ship paused to look out across the
white expanse that held them from the shore.

"It's lucky we couldn't go through it," Erik said finally. "Our ship might have been ground to pieces. And if we had been caught in it we would have starved." But Leif was wondering to himself whether he could not leap from one ice cake to another, and so finally reach the shore.

"Sail to the south," Erik ordered. "We'll try to go round it."

Hour after hour they sailed along the edge of the ice pack that glittered as the sun rose in the sky. Now and again they saw the dark form of a seal asleep on an ice cake in the sun. And once a bear, pure white like the ice itself, slid off a drifting cake into the sea near them to plunge after a fish, while over them the gulls wheeled down on strong gray wings. And all the time the mountains of the land they sought stood not far off, row upon row of them with their shining blue glaciers.

All day they rowed south along the edge of the ice pack until Leif began to wonder whether this journey would ever come to an end. At night they dared not row further for fear of losing their direction. They shipped their oars and lowered their sail, while the ship rocked in the waves. Then there were some on board who held in their hands small sticks carved in the image of Thor, and found comfort in these. But Leif smiled at their superstition, and wished the morning would come.

When it was light they rowed on again, still going south. And finally they came to a headland, and found to their great joy that the ice was gone. The ice pack ended neatly, like the edge of a table, and the water was blue and open.

But there was a current sweeping round that headland, so strong that it carried their ship along straight out toward the open ocean. The slaves bent to their oars, struggling against it; time passed, and it seemed the vessel had stood still. Harder and harder they struggled, the long oars bending, the veins standing out on the slaves' foreheads as they pulled against a greater strength than theirs, and the ship did not move. There was the land that they had sought. They had left the ice pack behind them, yet they could not reach the shore.

Then slowly, slowly they made headway. They struggled on with redoubled effort. They moved a little in the direction they sought. "Pull!" Erik cried. "Pull!" And they began to move across the current toward the shore. They rounded the headland at last, and found themselves in a quiet harbor, and brought the ship up broadside along the beach.

Leif was the first to jump down knee-deep into the water and wade ashore. After him Erik and the others followed: one of the men carried Thorhild to the beach in his arms while the children laughed and splashed after her. And finally the sheep and the oxen, the pigs and the horses, were led and driven from the boat into the water, and came splashing and dripping up to the land.

"Pitch the tents on the beach," Erik said. "Tomorrow we'll start building. There's no one here to dispute our rights. . . . Watch that the animals don't stray off."

Leif ran to catch a young heifer that had wandered across a narrow point of land. He stood for a moment holding the animal by one ear while he looked out across the ocean to the west.

Behind him the people were busy carrying boxes and casks ashore and pitching the tents. Before him the deep blue ocean stretched out to the far horizon, and over his head the gulls wheeled with apparently aimless motion.

"We're in a new land now," he was thinking. "Tonight I shall be sleeping in a new land. I do not know what it is like. Are there other people here? Shall I be able to talk to them? . . . Will they know anything about the countries out there to the west, beyond the edge of the sea?"

He pulled the heifer's ear and led it back to the encampment again. There was a smell of stew coming from the pot that hung over the fire.

9.

THE POLAR BEAR
ON THE ICE FLOE

IT'S BECAUSE you are a girl," Leif said.
"That's why you can't see so far. You don't have to.
You'll never command a galley and have to look out
for islands and rocks—"

He had known Astrid ever since he had first come
to Greenland—in fact she had been on the ship that
had brought them there. She had hunted gulls' eggs
with him, climbed over the glaciers, and sailed up the
fjords in his small skiff—still the fact remained always in his mind that she was a girl.

"That's why you can't see far," he said again.

"I can so see far," Astrid answered, indignant. "I
can see just as far as anybody. There isn't anything
at all on that ice floe."

They were sitting on a rock looking out over the ocean. Behind them the blue Greenland glaciers were glistening in the sun, before them lay the ocean with a great ice floe moving slowly from west to east.

"There's a polar bear on that ice floe," Leif said. "You wait till it comes in closer and you'll see it."

"How do you know it's coming any closer?" Astrid asked him, exasperated. "It's moving right across— without coming any nearer at all."

"It isn't," Leif said. "I can tell by the way the edge stands up from the water. I can tell which way the current is going to take it."

Astrid said nothing: she was tired of having Leif so sure of himself. Yet she had to agree that when it came to the ocean he was generally right.

"Watch now," Leif said, "and wait." She waited, annoyed but silent, looking at Leif more than the ice pack. He was taller than most boys of fourteen, taller than his father now. He wore a rough leather jerkin, and his boots, which reached up to the knee, were laced with leather thongs. A blue wool cord was tied around his head to keep his long yellow hair from blowing in his eyes. His skin was tanned until it was almost the color of his shirt, and Astrid thought him very handsome, but she was very much annoyed with him.

"I can see that ice floe just as well as you can," she said. "There isn't anything on it."

"Don't talk," Leif said. "I want to see which way it's drifting."

So Astrid was silent, and they watched for a long time.

The ice floe did come nearer, as Leif said it would. White and glittering it moved across the deep blue ocean.

"Can you see the bear now?" Leif asked at last, and Astrid had to acknowledge that she could.

It was a very young white bear cub, standing at the edge of the ice pack. From time to time it put its nose down toward the water as if it would plunge in, and then it drew back again apparently afraid.

"I'm going to get it," Leif said, and he started to run toward the shore.

"Don't go," Astrid called after him. "The current's too strong that way: you'll be drowned."

But Leif did not hear her. He ran to the shore where his skiff was pulled up on the beach, pushed it into the water, and with a strong thrust of his left leg, set it moving toward the ice floe. The current took it as soon as it reached the deep water. Astrid, watching from the shore, saw the nose of the skiff swing sharply, saw Leif on his knees in the center of the skiff paddling with strong sure strokes.

"He can't keep it up," she thought. "He'll be swept out to sea."

She watched him with a sort of fascination. No one was near, no one would have heard if she had cried for help.

Leif did not try to cross the current. He let it carry him along well past the end of the ice floe, and when he estimated that he had come to the right point, he turned his skiff at a sharp angle, and paddled back, approaching the ice on the other side.

It was the work of only a minute to pull the nose of his skiff up on a cake of ice, to run across the pack, avoiding the blue cracks with sure feet.

He came up behind the bear cub, and stopped for a moment, looking at it. It was smaller than he had thought; its fur was a soft ivory color against the blue-white ice. He leaned down with a quick motion to take it into his arms. But just at that moment the cub plunged. Perhaps it sensed that he was coming, or perhaps it saw a fish in the water and started in its clumsy way to go after it. Its dark little hind feet slipped off the ice, and the water whirled over it.

In a moment Leif was after it and had gripped the fur of its back with his hands. The bear was stronger than he had expected: the water made the fur slip between his fingers. Plunging and splashing, the two of them grappled together, and though the bear was only a cub, its nails were well grown; they cut a long gash in Leif's shoulder.

But Leif was strong, and he got the better of the bear at last. With a great heave he managed to push it up on the ice, and pulled himself up after it, and stood looking down at the cub, which sat quiet now as if it knew that it had met its master.

"You're a beauty," Leif said. "I never saw such

thick white fur. Nor such claws either." He pressed his right hand against his left shoulder where the blood was soaking down into his wet tunic. "I'll take you home," he said.

The bear made no particular resistance when he lifted it again. He put it in his skiff and pushed off, skirting the current as skillfully as he had come. Astrid was standing on the shore when he landed, but he paid hardly any attention to her. He managed to find a rope to tie around the bear's neck but that was hardly necessary: it came ambling along after him of its own accord.

All through the summer after that Leif worked to teach the bear its tricks. He sat on the rocks with a pile of silver herrings beside him, and when the bear sat up on its haunches pawing the air with its front feet, Leif flipped it a herring, which it caught and swallowed whole. Before very long it learned to lie down, to roll over and over, to dance on its hind legs while Leif sang to it. And every time it did a trick, Leif flipped a silver herring to it. They grew to be inseparable, Leif and the bear. People around Eriksfjord seldom saw one of them without the other, all through the years that Leif was growing up.

At first in those years Leif used to think sometimes that he missed the old place where he had been born: his friends there, the moors, the little Iceland ponies. Later he knew that he did not miss them at all. For here there was a grandeur in the ocean that came crashing up against the bleak rocks, there was a boldness in the peaks with their blankets of ice, there was the wet smell of salt in the air, and the sound of the sea. He did not have as many friends as he had in Iceland, but it didn't matter. Here he felt himself at the edge of a fresh world, and every day he knew more about the ocean: its color, its movement under the wind, the rhythm of its currents.

His father's house, Brattalid, was the center of a good deal of activity now. For after the three years of his exile, Erik had seen that Greenland might be successfully colonized, and a prosperous trade built up between there and Iceland and Norway.

Gradually larger and larger numbers of colonists came to settle in Greenland. Before long Erik had encouraged as many as a thousand to come. Some of them brought flocks that fed in the sparse pastures around Eriksfjord, some were fishermen, some hunted seal for their fur, and some killed walrus for their meat or carved the strong white ivory of the walrus tusks into knife handles or ornaments that they could sell.

Down in the harbor at Eriksfjord the ships were continually being loaded and unloaded, the men came and went, and the young Leif, talking to the sailors, learned the tricks of navigating the dangerous Greenland Sea, the ways of winds and ocean currents off Iceland or the Norwegian coast, the perils of storms and calms and icebergs.

He learned these things as a boy might learn the propositions in his geometry book. But they were more real than geometry to him: they were to be a part of his life.

So he grew to be twenty-four years old—but he had never yet been on a deep-sea voyage. And he had never yet had any very great concern with a girl.

10.

LEIF'S FIRST COMMAND

WHEN Leif was twenty-four his father said, "There is a cargo to be taken to Norway—it will go to Olaf Tryggvason, the King."

Leif, standing outside the house at Brattalid, looked sharply at his father. "To Norway?" he said. And in his mind he felt the pull of the ocean current that flows south of Iceland, the tug of the westerly wind in the sail, although he knew of these things only from the talk of other men who had gone there.

"I had thought to go myself," Erik continued. "But you are a man now. Sooner or later you'll have to take command of a trading expedition. Your mother and I came from Norway: you ought to be known there, now that you are a man. . . . You could take gifts to King Olaf."

Leif said, "Yes, I could do it," and under his shirt
his heart was pounding, and the color of his cheeks
grew darker, though no one noticed either of those
things.

There was a great stir of excitement in the harbor
at Brattalid the night before Leif sailed for Norway.
The long ship, freshly painted, lay tugging at its
anchor. The cargo of sealskins and walrus hides and
tusks were already packed in the hold, and fifty falcons, caught in the Greenland mountains, to be used
in Norwegian hunting, were carefully crated and tied
in a sheltered part of the deck. The casks of water and
barrels of food had been rolled on board.

Some thought had been given to the gifts which
Erik and Thorhild would send King Olaf, but finally
they had chosen a belt, beautifully carved of walrus
tusk, a ring set with a gleaming emerald, and a mantle
of scarlet satin embroidered with threads of gold.
These were locked carefully in a casket to be brought
on board at the last moment before they sailed.

By sunset all was ready, and word was sent to the
rowers that they would take the tide that set out to the
sea at dawn.

Now in the great hall at Brattalid, the fires were
lighted on the hearth, and on every pillar a torch of
pine knots was set aflame. And into the hall men and
women from all the settlements around came pouring
in—a hundred guests to wish Leif Eriksson good
fortune.

Now the great joints of meat were set out on the board, and cakes and sweetmeats of every kind. And soon the ale was flowing, and foaming up out of the drinking horns as they were raised to eager lips. And the strumming of a harp beat through the noise and confusion, and the voice of the skald was raised above the voices of the crowd.

Erik sat at the head of his board, laughing and calling for more ale. "My son," he kept saying, "my son is grown now. He will have command of a pretty vessel. It will be his first long voyage—"

And Thorhild was saying, "He will go to the court of King Olaf Tryggvason. It seems only right for our son to go to the royal court. He ought not to spend all his life in a rough frontier place like Greenland. Our son will be at home in the royal palace."

But Leif did not listen to the talk. He only wanted the night to be over. He wanted the morning to come, so that he could give the command to weigh anchor, and watch the long pull of the oarsmen, the straining of the sail.

The morning came at last, with a flush of pink in the eastern sky. A light mist played over the water of the harbor. The galley stirred a little and pulled at its moorings.

The whole company of men and women who had been at the banquet walked down to the shore to see Leif's galley go. The fourteen young men were soon at their places at the oars, and Thyrker, who would accompany Leif, had climbed on board.

Leif stood for a moment at the water's edge looking round him. There were the mountains taking form out of the night, the glaciers glistening, the harbor that he knew so well, the people who had come to see him go. Among those people Astrid was standing, but he did not see her. He stood for a moment on the little pier that jutted into the harbor, then waved, and climbed into the boat.

"Weigh anchor!" he cried, and at the moment when his first command was spoken, his mother broke from the little group where she was standing. She ran to the ship and put her hand on the painted bow.

"Take him safe," she murmured, as the ship moved slowly from the land.

11.

THE ISLAND IN
THE HEBRIDES

THAT day a fair wind was blowing, and Leif in command of his ship was filled with pride and excitement: his first long voyage was beginning.

The ship he was commanding was a beautiful one. He had bought it from Bjarni with money he had earned in seal hunting. It had been freshly painted blue, with a streak of red along the water line. And he had had the serpent's head painted green with red at the mouth and eyes, and bright touches of gold on the scales. Leif's father had given him a new sail for the ship, a sail that was yellow on one side and deep rose on the other, and the tackle was of walrus hide.

The fourteen rowers at the oars were young and hard-muscled: in their hands the oars flashed with perfect precision. And Leif himself stood tall and strong at the rudder, while Thyrker moved from one part of the ship to another, inspecting the tackle and the cargo with a practiced eye.

They rounded the cape at the mouth of the harbor, avoiding the fast racing current and setting their course toward the southeast. All day the gentle wind followed them. It was so slight a wind that they made hardly any headway: the men continued to row to help the ship on its way.

Hour after hour the sun was bright and warm, and the gentle waves lapped at the gunwales. Now and again a school of porpoises swam by, moving faster than the ship. Leif at the helm looked out across the ocean, and saw not a cloud in the sky. Behind him the mountains of Greenland dropped slowly out of sight as his ship moved gently forward over the quiet sea. This was not the voyage that Leif had dreamed of.

"If there was a storm," he was thinking, "I'd know how to trim the sail and keep the bow headed up into the wind. If we were caught in cross currents I'd know how to navigate them. If we met icebergs that knocked a hole in the ship, I'd set all men to bailing till the hole was patched. If we met enemies, we could fight. But this—"

So on and on they moved with the gentle wind blowing, slow—so slow it seemed to Leif's restive spirit that they hardly moved at all.

Not for nearly five days did they sight the coast of Iceland to the north of them, though everyone knew that sailors generally crossed the Greenland Sea in two.

"Let's go ashore," the men began to say. "Let's make the harbor at Reykjavik, and get our feet down on the ground. We could stay there for twenty-four hours, and maybe the wind would pick up after that." One of them had been in Reykjavik before: he said the girls were merry and warm-hearted there.

But Leif kept his hand steady on the tiller: passed the brown cliffs, the clustered houses in the harbor, and set out to sea again, the gentle wind following.

When the men were not rowing, they were playing chess, or rolling dice, or fishing. The time passed gayly enough.

But Leif, taking his first command seriously, began to notice that the long voyage was depleting the stores of food. They had been three times as long at sea as they had planned, and Norway was not yet in sight. Of course the ship had been well supplied. Barrels of meal, of peas and beans, dried meat and fish, had been stored in the hold, together with big round cheeses and loaves of dark hard bread. Casks of fresh water had been filled to the top.

But day after day the barrels were emptied, the water casks grew fewer in number, the bread and cheese were consumed. Young men with little to do eat a great deal when they are at sea.

Every day, three times a day, the small fires were built on the metal plates on the deck, and into the big copper pots went meat and fish, beans and grain, while the casks of ale and casks of water were emptied and tossed into the sea. At length Leif estimated that there was only enough food left for two more days. It was strange that an hour after this discovery was made, land was sighted—a small green island, rising from the sea.

The men on board thought it might be one of the Orkneys, but it did not look like the descriptions they had heard of them: it was not rocky enough, it was too green. Neither did they think it was one of the Shetland Islands. After long discussion they decided they had come further south to the Hebrides. And they were right: it was an island of the Hebrides, an island called Tirey.

They bent to their oars now, eager to make a landfall. For they wanted the feel of land after all their days and nights at sea. And Leif made no objection to landing—he knew that the food and water supply must be replenished.

On across the ocean they raced toward the green island, the oars cutting the water with a steady drip and splash. By the time the sand in the double hourglass had emptied itself, they were near enough to see trees and houses. They rowed on with new energy.

But as they rowed the skies began to darken, and the heavy clouds moved across the sky from the east.

Before they landed the rain had begun to fall: when they reached the harbor it was pouring down in floods. In spite of this a group of islanders had come down to meet them, and were soon helping them to beach the vessel and plying them with questions.

Where had they come from? But Greenland was a long way off. What was it like there? Where were they going? The men would be welcome to stay in the fishermen's houses along the shore. A messenger had been sent already to notify the lord of the island that they had come.

Leif smiled at the excitement his coming had caused, and tied his sea hat closer under his chin.

"You're kind," he said. "We shall be glad to stay until tomorrow. Perhaps the lord of your island will sell me some fresh supplies, and we can get fresh water."

"Tomorrow?" one of the gray-haired islanders replied. "When a storm sets in from the east at this time of year, it lasts three weeks—maybe a month or more. You won't get away tomorrow, or the next day, or for a long while after that."

He had hardly finished speaking when the messenger returned bringing a message from the lord of the island. According to the usual custom the master of the ship was urged to stay at the lord's house.

"Come with me, Thyrker," Leif said. "The men will be well enough off at the islanders' houses."

So Leif and Thyrker followed the messenger up

the road through the pouring rain. And Leif was in a
bad temper, for what bitter stroke of ill fortune was
this on his first voyage—to have so little wind that it
took his ship three times as long as it ought to make
the voyage, and then, before the voyage was even
completed, to be told that he was likely to stay here
on this island for an indefinite length of time because
of a raging storm.

"I won't do it, Thyrker," he said. "What do we
care for the easterly storm? We'll start tomorrow
anyway."

Thyrker said nothing.

The messenger led them up a road to a low house
set in the middle of a garden. Even in the pouring
rain, Leif could see the green of low hedges and
flowering shrubs, and could smell the unaccustomed
perfume of roses and stocks.

As they approached the house along the graveled
path, the door opened, and the lord himself stood in
the doorway, fair-haired as Leif and wearing a long
blue mantle fastened at the shoulder with a handsome
jeweled brooch.

"Come in," he said.

12.

THORGUNNA

THE room was large and low-ceilinged. It was handsomely furnished, for the lord of the island was a rich merchant who had traded in many parts of the world and had brought home valuable treasures. The floor was covered with new grass which gave off a pleasant fragrance. A cheerful fire blazed on the hearth, its light touched the bright tapestries that hung on the wall and the richly covered cushions, and lighted the burnished shields suspended in their shining row.

Near the fire on a low chair sat a girl whose fingers paused when Leif and Thyrker entered, and remained poised for a moment over her embroidery frame. The girl was dressed in blue—a long rich kirtle belted with a silver belt, and drawn in graceful folds over her slender figure.

71

"Thorgunna," the lord said. "These strangers have come from Greenland. We must make them comfortable here."

Thorgunna rose, putting her bright-colored yarns on the table.

"You're wet," she said, looking at Leif as if she had not known before that it was raining.

"Yes," Leif answered, looking back at her.

"Come closer to the fire," she said.

That night Leif lay awake in a small bedchamber, listening to the rain that beat on the roof and blew in heavy gusts against the side of the house. And then he slept a little while and dreamed of a girl in a blue kirtle, and then he woke again.

Half dreaming he imagined himself steering his vessel through a furious storm, the sail furled, the rowers trying to make headway against mountainous waves. It could not be far to the Norwegian coast, he thought, as he looked into the dark and listened to the wind. Yet even a little way might be almost impossible to navigate. Anyway, he would get the provisions loaded in the morning, he decided: he would go if he could.

And then he turned and tossed on his bed and listened to the rain again: and then he slept for a little and dreamed of the girl in a blue kirtle, and woke again, staring into the dark.

He was up just after dawn, making his way through sheets of cold rain to the beach where his galley lay. The sky seemed to hang low over his head, the wind from the east was dark and wet.

"There won't be anyone sailing out of this harbor for a good many days yet," an old man on the shore said. Leif recognized him as one of those who had met his vessel yesterday.

"I know these seas," the old man said. And Leif, looking out across the tumult of the waves, began to think he knew them too. He would stay at Tirey— at any rate until the storm abated.

So he returned to the comfortable house in the garden, to the cheerful warmth of the fire, the good food and drink, the quiet and the peace.

The lord was not often at home, having business affairs in other parts of the island. But Thorgunna was generally there at her embroidery frame. She was making a large piece of tapestry which some day would be hung up on their wall, she told him. The design was that of a woman in a flowing dress, walking down a garden path.

"I want to put in every flower that grows in the garden," she said. "Poppies and pansies and roses— and a squirrel down here, and a rabbit looking out from under this big green leaf."

"Don't work at it now," Leif would say. He was somehow jealous of the tapestry, wanting all her attention for himself.

So she would smile, and put down her needle, and ask him about Greenland, and what it was like there.

And he tried to tell her, although that world that he had known so well seemed far away and strange to him.

Sometimes she would stop her embroidery of her own accord. "I'm tired of working," she would say. "Let's play a game of chess."

Then while they sat close to the fire, moving the ivory kings and queens and knights and pawns across the checkered board, he noticed how delicate and strong her fingers were, and found himself check-mated time and again.

So the days passed, and the rains continued, and Leif lingered on at the house of the lord of the island, while Thyrker and the men of the crew amused themselves as best they could.

One day after they had sat together by the fire for a long time Leif rose and left Thorgunna abruptly, without any explanation. She saw him go to the door of his bedchamber and enter, closing the door behind him.

The small chest in which the gifts for the king of Norway were packed, was carefully locked and hidden under Leif's bed. He drew it out now, and with a small silver key which he wore on a chain around his neck, he unlocked the casket. From it he took the belt of carven walrus tusk.

Intricately fashioned and delicate, it lay in his brown hand: row upon row of little carven figures representing men that held each other's hands. He set

it on the bed, smiling, then carefully locked the casket
again and pushed it under the bed, and took the belt
to Thorgunna.

"Do you like it? Will you wear it?" he asked her.
And she held it round her waist, to show him how,
although it was too big for her, she could loop it between her fingers so that the ends just met at the back.

But after a moment she took it off, and held it out
to him again.

"We have no need of gifts to prove our friendship,"
she said.

"It's as you like," he answered.

But he did not take the girdle back, and presently
he put it on again around her waist, and she wore it.

So the days passed, with the rain beating down
unceasingly, and Thorgunna adding more flowers to
her tapestry, and the kings and queens and knights
and pawns taking their angular ways on the red and
white chess board.

One evening Leif rose again, and again he unlocked
the casket, and this time he drew from it the ring
with its gleaming jewel.

"It's nothing at all of itself," he said when he
brought it to her. "But on your finger it would take
on life—Will you wear it, to remember me by?"

Thorgunna slipped it on her slender finger. "It will
not take a ring to make me remember," she said.

Sometimes he was cruel to her, telling her in his
harsh way that women were timid and afraid of life,

and mocking her because she seemed not to have grown up.

When he talked thus, Thorgunna was overwhelmed with grief and wanted to cry. But she never cried. She waited, and afterwards he was tender to her again.

So time passed, and after a while the long storm abated. One night Leif went to the door and looked out, and there was the moon with ragged clouds blowing past its face.

"Strange that I should be so sad at the sight of the moon," he thought, and he went to the casket and drew out the scarlet mantle, all embroidered over with threads of gold.

Thorgunna was standing by the window when he brought it to her. She too had been watching the racing clouds.

"The wind has changed," Leif said. "The rain has stopped. Tomorrow—"

There was a silence, for he could not say what he had to say. He held the crimson mantle out to her with its lovely tracery of golden thread.

"Tomorrow you will start again for Norway," she said. And then, more softly, "Tomorrow I shall be alone."

13.

TO NORWAY

AFTER the excitement of Leif's going, Thorgunna stood for a long time on the shore. Everyone on the island had come to see the galley off. Everyone had talked of how grand it would be for Leif and his men to go to Olaf's court, and had given advice about the voyage. Now the ship was under way, and the people had turned back to their various occupations—here a man worked at calking his boat, there a woman busied herself with mending a fish net.

But Thorgunna stood alone and quiet on a little rise of ground, looking out across the water. It was a bright blue day—the air seemed to have been washed clean after the long storm. The west wind had blown every cloud out of the sky. On the ocean the waves were still rough, but the sun shone down on them so that they glittered and sparkled with light. Off across the water Leif's galley made steady progress north-ward, the yellow sail set, the oars flashing in the sun.

"The yellow sail that takes him from me," Thor-gunna thought. "The oars that are pulling him way."

After she had watched a long time, until she could no longer distinguish Leif at the rudder, she turned slowly, and walked back through the garden to the house.

On the table she saw the chess board where they had left it, the ivory chessmen standing on their squares, ready to move. She picked up one of the pawns and held it in her hand a moment. Then care-fully she collected the other chessmen, and put them all away in a wooden box.

"I shall not want them now," she said.

Listlessly she turned to her embroidery frame, and sank down into the low chair before it. She had done very little work on the embroidery in the last month. The little rabbit under his big green leaf was still half finished, and there were wide spaces of brown mesh where she had planned the flowers would be.

"There will be nothing to prevent my working, now," she said, and taking up a needle she tried to thread it with blue yarn. But her eyes were blurring, so that she could not even see the needle's eye, and after a while she put it down again.

Out at sea Leif Eriksson gave a quick glance over his shoulder at the green island, and the low roofed

house where he had lived almost a month. And he did
not know Thorgunna had been standing on the shore
to watch him sail away.

"She was different from the girls in Greenland," he
was thinking. "I think she was different from any
other girl," and he remembered the touch of her lips.
"I am glad I gave her the ivory belt, and the ring, and
the scarlet cloak," he said half aloud. "For kings have
many things, and I think they do not always grace
them. . . . But Thorgunna—"

He grasped the tiller harder, for the wind was very
strong and would have beaten him off his course.

"Trim the sail," he cried to the sailors. "We're making good time now."

The wind filled the sail, and the slender vessel raced
across the ocean, cutting a silver furrow that sparkled
in the sun.

"There is no one like her," Leif thought, feeling
now that he had known Thorgunna, he knew all the
women in the world. And it never even occurred to
him, as he held the racing vessel on its course, that
he might have stayed with her.

14.

KING OLAF TRYGGVASON

OUT across the steel blue ocean, Leif's vessel raced on its way toward the Norwegian coast. It was not many days before they sighted the shore and were sailing along past lofty cliffs and countless little islands, till they came to the fjord at Trondheim. It was at Trondheim that King Olaf Tryggvason was in residence.

They rowed up the fjord and entered the harbor in fine array, the splash and pull of their oars perfectly timed, their yellow sail spread, their shields hung along the gunwales. Leif stood at the rudder, erect and handsome, the sun on his yellow hair and his cheeks burned by the wind.

There had been plenty of time for the news of their

coming to be spread among the people as they rowed up the fjord. By the time they reached the shore, there was a crowd awaiting them. Sailors and fishermen, farmers on their way to market, lumbermen and loiterers—all crowding together to have a look at the newcomers.

They pressed round the boat when Leif and his men waded ashore, and there was a babel of talk: Where had they come from? What had they brought in trade? Would they stay long? What port would they sail for then?

The Greenlanders looked curiously at the crowding people, and beyond them at the low log houses, and the mountains with their mantle of green trees. A strange land it seemed to them: not like the bleak Greenland mountains with their glaciers, nor yet like Iceland with its high sunny moors and airy snow-capped peaks. This land was different from any they had ever seen.

They stood looking round, and as they did so, the crowd parted, and a plump, red-faced man in a purple mantle fastened at the shoulder with a handsome jeweled buckle, approached them. A servant held the horse from which he had just dismounted, as well as another handsomely saddled and bridled mount. The people made way for the stranger respectfully, and he approached Leif at once.

"King Olaf Tryggvason bids you welcome," he said. "We do not know from what country you come, but we can see by your vessel that you are an important merchant, and it is the custom of Norway to offer such a one the royal hospitality."

Leif smiled, not ill-pleased at the mark of recognition. "My father is Erik the Red," he said with a modest air. "We come from Greenland."

The messenger then invited him to come at once to King Olaf Tryggvason's hall, saying that his men would be made comfortable in the fishermen's houses, and that he would see that their cargo was unloaded.

So it was that Leif was soon in the saddle, and following Olaf's messenger up the winding road through the forest, to the place high on the mountainside, where the King's house stood. As they climbed higher and higher with the sure footed little Norwegian horse making its way along the road behind the messenger, the horse's gait, and the warm smell of his coat, made Leif think of his boyhood in Iceland and of how he used to ride his pony there. "But this is very different," he thought. "All these trees—"

He was still marveling at the sight of the trees when they reached the door of Olaf's hall. A groom ran out to hold the horse, and Leif dismounted and followed the messenger through a wide door.

Leif had expected that the court of a king would be luxurious. He had talked with many Vikings who had told him that most of the European royalty lived on a grand scale. But Olaf Tryggvason had simple tastes. The hall was not much larger than Erik's hall at Brattalid. A great fire leaped and blazed on the hearth and before it was spread an enormous rug of black bear skin. When they entered King Olaf rose from a high carved chair and came toward Leif and the messenger. He was a short, stoutly built man wearing a tunic of green velvet, and though his head was bald, his step had the spring of a young man. Behind him two enormous wolfhounds lay on either side of his chair, watching Leif with attentive eyes, but making no motion.

"Our guest is from Greenland," the messenger said. "He is called Leif—the son of Erik the Red."

"Welcome, Leif Eriksson," King Olaf said, extending his hand. "I remember your father well.

He smiled at Leif, and Leif liked him.

That was the beginning. Soon Leif was telling him of the sealskins, and walrus hides, and ivory tusks that he had brought in trade. "And falcons?" Olaf asked him. "Did you say falcons?"

"Yes," Leif answered, "I'd like to give them to you for a gift." To himself he thought, "The King will like these better than the things I gave Thorgunna." Then he went on, "We have brought more than a hundred falcons. The young birds have been carefully reared in Greenland and trained by the Greenlanders to the lure. You'll find them swift enough to soar and pounce when you have unleashed them, docile enough to perch again when they have disposed of their prey."

"Falcons!" Olaf repeated.

Next day the crates with their falcons were the first cargo to be unloaded from Leif's vessel. They were brought at once to King Olaf's hall, and the King himself inspected the unpacking. Bright eyed and hungry, with curving beaks and sharp talons, the birds would have flown to their freedom, but each one had its head covered with a leather hood before it was set on a perch in King Olaf's aviary.

Olaf was in fine spirits when he saw them. "Look at those soft barred feathers," he cried, lifting one of the birds. "Look at those beautiful strong wings—" He turned to Leif, eagerness and excitement in his voice. "Tomorrow morning early we'll try some of them," he said. "Tomorrow right after sun-up."

So it was that next day, and for many days thereafter Leif rode with King Olaf and his companions, through the green forests of Norway. And every man had a brown barred bird with a leather hood perched on his wrist.

Sometimes they hunted rabbits and squirrels and little foxes, letting the falcons find their prey, but drawing them off before the strong beaks and claws could tear the animals into shreds. Sometimes they hunted herons. Then when they had found a flock of heron on the margin of some forest pool, they released the falcons and watched while the herons rose, and the falcons on strong wings tried to rise above them, and drop on them to tear them apart.

So day followed day, and it seemed to Leif that all the business of the world was nothing in comparison with this glorious sport, and that no life was so good as this—to ride through forests where the long green branches of the trees arched over his head, to feel the movement of a strong young horse beneath him, to hold on his wrist the cruel little bird whose wings were so strong it could outstrip any creature on the ground or in the air.

"Stay with me a year," Olaf said to Leif.

And Leif agreed. He was young, and the years ahead of him were many. He could afford to spend one of them with King Olaf Tryggvason.

15.

THE SIGN OF
THE CROSS

A YEAR is not long. The summer and the autumn were over, the winter was past. The light of the sun was strong again, the snow melted, the ice was broken up, and the streams went rushing down the mountains into the fjords in full flood.

In the mornings when he woke early Leif heard the birds singing—a richer chorus than any he had ever heard.

Greenland and his father's house seemed far away from him now. So completely was he absorbed in the life of Norway that it seemed as if his old life had never been. Yet with the coming of the spring he knew that he must go home again, and he accepted the thought as he accepted the change of the seasons:

it seemed to him a natural thing, not to be fought against or altered.

One day he sat near a window playing chess with Olaf by the lingering light of the afternoon sun. There had been a hard fight between the red and white chessmen but it appeared that Leif's men would triumph, for he was driving Olaf's remaining kings and castles into what would surely be untenable positions. It had not been long since he had played the game with Thorgunna. He had loved to play with her, but this was a man's contest: he could use all his ruthlessness now, and not be distracted by her white fingers.

Leif moved the men quickly, sure of what he was doing, planning his moves with craftiness.

"Check!" he cried, disposing of one of Olaf's pawns. Olaf paused, leaning back in his chair, his eyes on Leif's face.

"You will be leaving soon," he said. "The spring winds will be setting back toward Greenland."

"Yes," Leif answered, his mind still intent on the game. "It will not be many days now."

"Shall you call on Thor to guide you back?" There was an edge of scorn in Olaf's voice.

Leif looked up. He had never been particularly interested in the gods, for he had felt little need to call on them. A man ought to depend on his own strength and skill, he had always thought privately. So he looked at Olaf and said nothing.

"Thor and Odin, Frig and Freya—they are nothing but images of wood and stone which men have made," Olaf said. "I too once worshipped them. But when Norway was stricken by the plague and the people were dying by the hundreds, I heard them calling on Thor and Odin for help. Thor and Odin could not help them. They kept on dying. . . . I turned aside from the old gods then . . ."

Leif let his eyes wander from the checkered board toward the window, where the shadows of the spring evening were beginning to fall.

But Olaf went on. "I turned to the living Christ," he said. "I was baptized. And thousands in Norway followed my example. And the plague stopped—"

The vigorous, practical face of Olaf took on a mystical expression which Leif had never seen before.

"When you go back to Greenland you could show the power of the Christ there," he said. "You could make them see that none but the true Christ can help them. I could send a priest with you to persuade them."

Leif, remembering his father, doubted that he at least would ever be persuaded to abandon the old gods. But he himself was interested. As the days passed he talked more and more with the Christian priests and finally resolved that he would abandon the old gods, and be baptized in the new faith that seemed so full of promise.

On the day of his baptism in Olaf's hall he was

dressed in a long garment of pure white. A hundred candles burned in silver candlesticks, and the smoke from a hundred censers mounted up—the sweetest fragrance Leif had ever smelled.

"Dost thou believe in Jesus the Christ, the Son of the Living God?" the priest murmured.

And Leif answered, "I do."

"Dost thou accept him, and desire to follow him as thy Saviour and Lord?"

And again Leif answered, "I do."

Then the priest dipped his fingers in a silver bowl filled with clear water, and marked the Sign of the Cross on Leif's forehead. So Leif became a Christian.

When he set off for Greenland a few days later under a fair wind, the priest in a long black habit with a silver cross on his breast went with them. The priest's purpose was to Christianize all the colonists of Greenland.

16.

THE SHIFTING WINDS

ON the eve of Leif's departure from Norway, the King ordered a great feast in his honor. In Olaf's hall the pine torches threw out a flood of light, and the great fire leaped and blazed on the hearth. The flames danced and glistened on the men's brass shields and burnished helmets, and lighted the silk and velvet of the women's dresses, and touched the long silky braids of their hair, and brought warm color to their cheeks.

King Olaf sat at the head of the long table. His robe of purple velvet was fastened with an enormous brooch, and he wore a heavy chain of gold around his neck. Beside him Leif was clad in coat of mail, and many of the women noticed that he was taller than any man in the company, and stronger, and handsomer. Thyrker sat beside the black-robed priest who was to accompany them to Greenland.

Now the servants ran up and down the table carrying steaming roasts and joints of meat, with ducks and geese and pheasants, and plump fish caught in the Norwegian fjords. Huge cheeses and great rounds of flat bread, and sweetmeats covered every foot of the long board. It was as if King Olaf imagined that the Greenlanders would not have an opportunity to eat again for a year.

When Leif raised his drinking horn to his lips he paused a moment, for the liquor that he tasted was smooth and pleasant on his tongue.

"I have ordered mead," King Olaf said, watching him. "Have you tasted it before? We do not have it often."

Leif smiled, and drank again, for it was true that he had never tasted mead before, and he was pleased with the honor that was being done him. Up and down the table laughter and talk and warm good fellowship overflowed.

"Good fortune to the men of Greenland! Fair winds! Smooth seas!" the vikings cried. And Leif, looking about him, felt a glow of warmth and friendliness toward these Norwegians that he had grown to know so well.

All night the feasting lasted. From time to time a skald with a silver-stringed harp sang to them of the exploits of heroes and voyagers. And then the mead flowed again, and fresh roasts were brought in.

Some time after midnight they left the table and

began to dance. And Leif took a tall fair-haired girl for his partner, all the time thinking she was not half so lovely as Thorgunna: but her feet were light, and she served.

They sang as they danced with lusty voices, and swayed and clapped their hands, and leaped into the air. And when they were breathless the mead flowed again.

Never did a viking set off across the ocean with such a banquet to honor him, Leif thought. He remembered the feast his father had given before he left Greenland.

"But it was not like this," he thought. "Not like the banquet a king can give."

Morning came at last. When the sun came in at the door the torches were put out. The last toast was drunk, and the whole company walked to the shore where the galley waited, Leif and King Olaf walking first.

The cargo had been loaded the day before—the sacks of grain, the timber, the bolts of woven cloth. Now the yellow sail was hoisted, the men were at their oars.

Then at the stern of the boat the dark-robed priest raised his hand in blessing. Leif thought for a brief moment of how his mother had run down and put her hand on the ship when he left home. He would be back in Greenland soon, he thought. It was a comfortable thought.

"Make way!" he cried, and the oars flashed in the sun.

Down the long fjord they rowed toward the open sea, and the wind filled the sail so that oars and sail together sent the vessel plunging through the waves. Every man in the boat was in high spirits, for they were going home, and they had been away a year.

"My baby will be a big fellow now—he will hardly know me," one man said. The man beside him nodded. "My girl will be waiting. There'll be a wedding when I get back," he said. And a third one spoke. "My wife will have borne our child by now," he said.

But Leif at the tiller said nothing. He was thinking, "When I get back to Brattalid I shall have taken my first trading voyage. And it has been successful: everyone will agree to that. This cargo of timber alone is worth a fortune. My father will think I have made a good bargain. He will be pleased that the King has shown me such favor—"

They had rounded the cape at the mouth of the fjord now, headed out for the open sea. "No stop at the Hebrides this time," Leif was thinking. "No stop at Iceland, either. We'll make it straight through. It will be a record—"

By noon the heavy clouds began to gather. It had been a radiant morning, blue skied and clear. But now the wind changed and blew from the west, and with it came the clouds—little light clouds at first, moving across the blue. Then heavier ones joining them, until the whole sky was covered, and the gray was thick and heavy.

Meantime the sea, which had been covered with little curling waves, grew rough and angry, and the boat tossed and rolled, throwing up bursts of spray across the deck.

But all the while Leif kept the galley on its course. There was to be no monotony in this voyage, like that they had encountered on the way out. Now, he thought, he would have some opportunity to try his seamanship.

Early in the afternoon the sun disappeared altogether, and the wind veered again. Now the gale was so strong that the sail bulged in a wide curve, and the thongs that held it stretched and stretched, and one of them snapped with a loud crack. The mast began to bend.

"Ship your oars! Strike sail!" Leif shouted above the roar of the storm, and the men jumped to obey his order.

Down came the yellow sail, and it was quickly furled. Then the slim galley lay in the trough of the waves, rolling, directionless, while the seas mounted higher and higher. Near the bow a sailor fingered a wooden stick carved in the image of Thor which he wore on a string around his neck, while in the stern the priest in his long black habit handled his rosary. But Leif and the other men on board waited and watched the turbulent sea.

The wind shifted, and shifted again, as the boat rolled now this way and now that. For a long time there was no sun to give them their position, and at night there were no stars.

"Even if we knew what direction to take, we could not take it," Leif was thinking. To Thyrker he said, "How shall we steer without stars or sun, if we do not know from what quarter the wind comes?"

Old Thyrker shook his head.

Just at that moment a man came running up the ladder that led below the deck. Under the bronze that the wind and sun had given him, Leif saw that his face was pale.

"She's sprung a leak, master," he said. "The water's pouring in around the masthead!"

"Man the buckets!" Leif shouted to the men.

Leif himself was first to reach the bailing compartment, a small cubicle in the very center of the ship. He saw that it was nearly filled with water which went sloshing up and down with the movement of the ship in the sea.

"Form a line!" he cried, stooping down to dip up the first dripping bucketful of sea water and passing it to the man beside him.

So they began, and hour after hour they bailed. Sometimes it seemed to them that they had lowered the water a little, and then it ran in again, and rose higher than ever. But they never paused in their bailing. Hour after hour they worked, swinging the buckets faster and faster. At last when they had reached a breakneck pace they succeeded in lowering the water enough to bring it down below the place where the seam in the boat had sprung. Then they calked the place with pitch, they dropped their buckets, and climbed wearily to the deck.

They found that the wind had died down while they worked. The sea was calmer. The stars were shining. And they had no idea where they were, nor what direction they should take: for they had no idea what lay north or south or east or west of them.

17.

"LAND, OFF THE STARBOARD BOW!"

EXHAUSTED, the men sat on the galley's deck and looked across the quieting sea. Over them the night sky was clear and brilliant, the familiar stars blazing through the dark, the galley rolling gently on the waves.

"Open a cask of ale," Leif said, and the men filled their drinking horns and drank, looking across the water.

"There's the North Star. We can tell the points of the compass now," one said. "But what good will that do us, if we don't know where we are. Does Greenland lie north of us, or south?"

They drank again, and rested.

The sea was wide and dark around them. The galley

97

was a tiny speck in what looked like a limitless ocean.

Leif said, "We must plot some course. We cannot drift or we shall never reach the land." But he spoke with little confidence.

"We'll rest till morning," he said, thankful that they had been able to remain afloat. They lay down on the deck and as they lay there, a light began to move down the sky.

Stronger and stronger the long rays of light came quivering down. And now they took on color—rose and violet, blue and yellow and green, like long shining ribbons swinging back and forth across the dark. There on the galley the tired men lay, still watching the moving light, the radiant colors. At last they slept.

But Leif was awake. He watched while the darkness faded into the gray of morning, and wondered what course he should take. He thought that Greenland must be north of them, but he could not be sure. They had been blown hither and thither by the changing winds: they might be east of Greenland or west of it, he could not tell. Surely if he sailed in almost any direction he would come to land at last. But when would that be? How long would the food and water last? He looked at the sleeping men on the deck. Their lives were in his hands. They depended on him.

A little breeze sprang up at daylight. It was slight at first, like a faint breath blowing across the water. But in an hour it was stronger, and soon it was a

steady gale. With the daylight the sleeping men on
the deck wakened. One after another they rose, and
looked out across the water. "A good breeze," they
said to one another. "We could beat against it, maybe,
and make our way northeast. It would be hard though,
and we'd not even be sure of a harbor in the end."

"Why should we beat against it?" Leif said. "If a
strong wind blows, why should we not sail with it?
Let's hoist the sail."

With a creak of pulleys, the sail was lifted. It was
filled with the wind, and the ship sped forward. The
wind blew stronger and the ship raced on. The heavy
sea went foaming round the bow.

Leif and his crew stood watching the waves race
past them, feeling the wind behind them, the sun
shining, the salt spray on their faces. What could be
more glorious than this for men who loved the sea?
Surely their commander was lucky, the men said to
each other. Hadn't their journey to Norway been
lucky? Hadn't they made the long crossing without
even stopping off at Iceland—the first people ever to
do such a thing? A great viking Leif Eriksson was,
they said to each other, even if he was as young as
any of them and on his first command. When the
wind veered, he would turn and sail northeast again.
And then they would arrive in the harbor at Eriksfjord, and faster than any crew that tried to beat its
way against the wind across the Greenland Sea.

But the wind did not change. It blew steady and

strong, day after day, night after night. The crew were half intoxicated with the speed of the motion: they paid no heed to the direction they were taking, and did not reckon that they must have left Greenland far behind. Some time the wind would shift, they said. Meantime they had a commander who would bring them luck. It was glorious to go racing across the ocean.

Leif too felt the excitement of the racing ship, but he knew that it was forty days since they had left Norway.

The fortieth night was a night of bright moonlight. And the wind was still blowing. Some time after midnight they heard a sailor shouting from the bow.

"Land, comrades, land!" he cried running back along the deck. "Land, off the starboard bow!"

Every man was on his feet. They crowded around Leif at the bow of the boat, straining their eyes to see.

There in the moonlight they saw cliffs rising, dark between the glistening water and the star-strewn sky.

On and on they sped, the sail swelling, the wind blowing strong. And the shore came nearer and nearer, and faintly at first, but louder and louder, they heard the sound of pounding surf.

Was it Greenland? Could it be? There were no glaciers on the cliffs, they could see that. If there had been glaciers, they would have shone white in the moonlight. But here the shore was dark against the sky. Yet if the land was not Greenland, what land was it?

Leif listened to the sailors' talk. And he remembered the day when he was still a boy, and Bjarni had come sailing back to Greenland and told of a land in the western sea which he had seen but where he had not set his foot. But Leif said nothing: in the morning he would know more about that land.

In the morning they rounded a little cape, sailed across a wide bay, and dropped anchor off the shore. The men were wild with excitement. They began to lower a boat, eager to find out more about the land that they had reached at last. But Leif was cautious.

"This is not Greenland, nor any other land we know," he said. "We do not know what people are here, nor what their numbers are. No man must go ashore till we have found out something about the people in this place."

Disappointed, the men raised the boat again and waited. Leif, his eyes fixed on the shore, searched for people, the smoke of a fire burning, a house.

But there was nothing—no sign of human habitation. He saw three great white herons near the shore, and sea gulls flying back and forth across his ship and settling on the water. There were no men.

18.

THE COAST OF A NEW WORLD

THE men grumbled. Forty days at sea they had been and now they came to land and could not go ashore. But Leif would not relent, not yet. The land would wait for them. He wanted to know what kind of people were there before any of them landed.

To quiet their restlessness he had them get out food and prepare a meal. Salt fish and dark bread and cheese, they ate, and filled their drinking horns with ale. And there in the bay off an unknown land, they sat and ate with healthy appetites born of salt air and young bodies.

Leif too was hungry, but he ate standing, his eyes on the shore. He could see that it was a land of rocky cliffs that came down sharply into the water. Only

here and there he saw a gnarled tree rooted in some
crevice in the rocks. It was an inhospitable land, and
a deserted one apparently. If any people lived here
they must be fishermen, for there was no grass for
feeding cattle, no forest where deer or even rabbits
might be hunted. But if the people were fishermen,
they were not on the shore. There were no traces of
them: no boat was pulled up on the rocks, no nets
were drying. . . .

The men of the crew finished eating at last. The
scraps were tossed into the water and the sea gulls
circled down and took them.

Then Leif said, "Take whatever weapons you have
with you. The people may have been watching from
behind some rock."

And the men took knives and spears, and Leif and
the others climbed down into the little boat and rowed
to the shore.

They clambered up on the rocks, and keeping close
together for safety's sake, began to climb the cliff.
When they had reached the top, they looked around.
There was the bay, their galley anchored in the harbor, and along the shore to north and south as far as
they could see were rocks. Here and there they saw
a wind-twisted tree, here and there a juniper bush—
nothing else.

"Even Greenland has some grassy places," one of
the men said, looking down along the barren shore.

"True," Leif answered. "This is the bleakest place

I ever saw. Let's call it Helluland—the Land of the Flat Rocks."

The men agreed, feeling indignant because they had come so far and found such a bleak place.

"We'll sleep aboard the ship tonight," Leif said. "It will be safer. Tomorrow we'll sail south along the shore. Perhaps the land will be more fertile further south."

Next morning they started early, sailing south along the coast with a strong northeast wind. They concluded this was no island they had found. It was an enormously big land. They sailed two days and two nights past islands, past little bays and inlets, and always along the coast they saw the same rocks, the same barren shore.

But on the third day they sensed that the air was a little warmer, and there was a smell of earth and trees. And the rocks gave way to green forests: the trees came down to the shore. The men stood looking at the trees with hungry eyes.

Soon they had landed on a sandy beach, and waded ashore. It was not necessary to lower a boat, they sailed up close and jumped down into the water, and it was easy to beach the galley on the sand. Soon leafy branches were waving over their heads, ferns brushed against their knees as they passed, and small white flowers were blooming. They put their hands down on green moss, and felt it moist and cool.

"A land of forests!" Leif kept saying, walking

under the tall swaying trees. "A land of beautiful forests! Let's call it Markland—the Land of Forests!" No one could think of a better name.

Again that night they lay in the galley, but most of them did not sleep. For in their minds they kept seeing the forests and the earth green with its ferns and mosses. They were like hungry men satisfied, after their long tossing at sea.

At daylight they were up again, ready to go on. It was a bright clear day, and they sailed across a wide bay under a gentle wind. That night they did not land, but sailed on in moonlight, talking of the land that they had found.

Next day they rounded a little promontory, and found a place where a stream of fresh water poured down into a bay. Here they beached the galley again, and stood silent on the shore looking around them. The air was warm and sweet, for a gentle offshore breeze was blowing. "Look!" one of them said, and near them the bushes parted and a brown deer, not heeding them at all, came down to the edge of the stream and put its head down to the water to drink.

Leif said, "We'll make a camp here. We'll stay here a while and explore this land." And soon the men were cutting trees to build a shelter big enough for them all, and carrying their gear from the galley, and pulling the galley up on the beach where it would be safe until they wanted it again.

And all the time no human being came near them:

they saw no trace of any habitation, no footprint, no
ashes of a burned-out fire.

That night they remained for the first time on the
land. And at evening the air was filled with bird
music, and in a pool at the edge of the river they
heard the high-pitched voices of a hundred frogs.
After the darkness came there was an owl hooting
from a branch in a far-off tree. But there were no
other sounds.

Leif said in the morning, "It's spring now. We can
stay all summer. Judging by the looks of these trees
we can take a good cargo of logs back to Greenland
in the autumn."

The men were eager to explore. They wanted to
start at once, to see what they could find. But Leif
was still cautious. It seemed impossible to him that
there could be a place like this without inhabitants.
And whether the inhabitants would prove friendly
or hostile, he had no way of knowing.

"Form into two groups," he said. "It will be safer
that way. Let the men in each group stay close together: don't separate on any account. We cannot
tell who may attack us. I will stay at the camp and
wait for you. Come back at sunset, and tell me what
you have found."

So the men set off. Soon they had disappeared into
the forest.

By sunset they came back again.

"What did you find?" Leif asked when he saw
them approaching. And again, "What did you find?"

"We found salmon leaping in the stream," they answered. "Big plump salmon—bigger than any we have ever seen. There were so many we could almost catch them with our hands. We shall have no want of fresh fish," they said.

"What else did you see?" Leif asked.

"We saw rabbits running through the woods, and deer, and game birds aplenty—there will be no dearth of food," another said.

"And there were lovely flowers," Thyrker was speaking now. "There were mayflowers like those that grow in Germany. And some flowers whose names I do not know."

"Did you see any men?" Leif asked. "Or any footprints, or the ashes of any fires?"

"No, we saw none of these," they said.

19.

VINLAND THE GOOD

SO it was on the second day, and on the third day, and on the fourth day. Every day the men came back at sunset, and every day they told of the rich treasures of this country, the great trees of the virgin forest, enough to send endless cargoes of timber back to Greenland. They told of the animals that would be so easy to trap—they would get rich with the furs alone, they said. One day they came back telling of a field of grain.

"What kind of grain?" Leif asked. "What kind of men have planted it?"

"We do not think that it was planted," they said. "It seems to grow wild—so much of it that it covers a whole valley. The heads of it are heavy, ready to be cut. It is something like wild wheat. We could harvest it, and put it into sacks," they said. And some of them remembered the smell of baking bread their wives had made.

But one day when the men came back Leif saw that Thyrker was missing.

"Where is Thyrker?" Leif asked, casting a quick look over the company.

"We do not know," they answered. "He kept stopping to look at some flower, or some special kind of tree. He kept exclaiming that this one had a certain Latin name, and that one grew in Germany. We told him to come on: he was so slow. And then we noticed that he was not there. We went to look for him. We called and called. And we could not find him anywhere. . . ."

"Thyrker," Leif said. And in his mind fear for his foster father filled him with anguish. What had become of him?

They threw fresh logs on the fire, thinking that the light might help to guide Thyrker back. They shouted till his name echoed and re-echoed through the forest. There were only shadows and quietness. Thyrker did not come.

In the morning they set out to search for him again. Through all the woods they went, shouting his name. But they could not find him. And Leif was full of sadness for the little German who had taught him so much, of whom he was so fond. Could some animal have fallen on him and torn him to pieces, he wondered. Had he fallen from some cliff, or met with hostile people whom none of the rest of them had seen?

They searched and searched, until the evening shadows filled the forest, and the birds were making their evening songs.

One after another then, they came back to the shelter: they could not find the little man.

They were seated around the fire in silence. What could they do? The forest was endless, and darkness was coming down again. They had called until they were hoarse. They had searched and searched. If Thyrker was dead, they could not even find his body. The stillness was heavy around them.

Then from far off they thought they heard a cry. They sprang to their feet and listened. The cry came again. The voice undoubtedly was Thyrker's. They knew it well.

Leif ran toward the woods in the direction from which the voice seemed to come. Was Thyrker hurt? Where had he been?

Then in the firelight the men saw him coming. He was running, and in his arms he held a bundle wrapped in the old cape that he always wore.

"Thyrker!" Leif cried.

And Thyrker ran toward him holding out the bundle in his arms.

But Thyrker was not hurt. His old face was wrinkled with smiles. And he was talking, a great stream of German that none of them could understand.

He ran into the circle of the firelight, and put down his bundle on the ground. And then, as if he had found all the treasure of the Indies, he drew aside his cape. The men gathered around him in a circle to see what he had found. And on the ground they saw a heap of purple fruit.

"They're grapes!" Thyrker cried. "They are grapes, like the ones that grew on the hillsides in Germany. I could not believe it when I saw them. They are growing wild there. Just like the ones in Germany that we had to plant. We'll make wine!" He was speaking their own language again now.

None of Leif's crew had ever seen grapes. They looked at Thyrker as if they thought him insane. But he was not abashed.

"Look at them," he cried. "All through my boyhood I saw them like this in the vineyards in Germany. Look at them!" he held a purple cluster up for them to see. "Smell them," he said. "How sweet!"

And then he took a bunch between his hands, and pressed his palms together, and the juice flowed down over his wrists. "They're full of juice," he said. "Full of the delicious purple juice, just like in Germany."

"Where have you been?" Leif asked. "We have searched everywhere for you. We thought some harm had come to you."

"No harm," Thyrker said. "Good fortune. I was examining the plants and the trees, and the others went on faster. And I walked on through the forest by myself—such *rare* plants I found. *Wunderbar—*

wonderful. And then I came to a hillside, and there
the grapes were growing—lots of them, all over the
hillside. I stopped, and I ate them—the taste was so
good, *wirklich*, truly—it was like being home in Germany again. So I sat down on a stone and the smell
of them was so good. I think I must have fallen
asleep.

"It was dark when I woke, but I could still smell the
grapes. And it was not cold. I pulled my cape around
me, and I slept there, with that good smell in my
nostrils.

"When it was morning, I started to pick them. I
picked and I picked till I had a great mound of them.
I thought I would bring them back here. We could
press them, we could make wine, like in Germany. But
how could I carry them? I filled my cape with them,
and my hat, and I took off my shirt to carry some
in that—but I couldn't carry them—they kept rolling
out. So I just brought these.

"If you will come back, I will show you. We can
each carry some, we can squeeze them, and make them
into wine, like in Germany—I will show you."

Leif had been annoyed with Thyrker at first. But
when he listened to this long recital he could not
help smiling. Thyrker was so excited that he could
hardly talk, and every now and then he lapsed back
into German.

"Let's go and see them," Leif said. "Do you think
you can find them again?"

"*Aber natürlich*, of course," Thyrker said, pulling Leif by the arm.

But it was not until morning that they followed Thyrker to the place where the grapes grew. There on the ground they saw the heap that Thyrker had picked. And up over the hillside, tangled among the branches of the trees they saw the curling tendrils of the vines, the rusty green leaves, the fragrant fruit. They tasted the fruit, and then they began to pick in earnest, and every man carried some of them back to the camp as best he could.

In the days that followed the place was full of activity. For they discovered that the vines that Thyrker had found were not the only ones. There were grapes in many nearby places. They scoured out the casks that had held salt fish and ale and set them in the sun to air, and they carried them to the hillsides and began to pick. And Thyrker showed them how to squeeze the juice, and set it aside to ripen into wine, and before long they were gayly drinking the heady new beverage.

So the days of the late summer passed. And still there were grapes on the vines.

"Let's pick a load of the grapes and take them back to Greenland," the men said. "If we fill the hold of the galley with timber, we can put the grapes into the little boat. We'll be the first ever to bring such a cargo to Greenland!"

That was what they did. All day their axes rang in

the forest. Tree after tree was felled and stripped of its branches and loaded into the hold of the galley. They brought timber of many different kinds, but the wood they valued most they called *mosur* wood, a kind of maple.

When the timber had all been loaded, they collected the grapes, and heaped the little boat with them, and tied it to the stern of the galley. And at last all was ready, and they hoisted the yellow sail. The light wind filled it. They were under way.

They crossed the bay, and rounded the promontory, and stood on the deck, watching the green shores dropping away behind them. And they reckoned Greenland lay ahead of them, and home. They wanted to go home: they had been away so long. But they were sorry to leave those green shores they had found.

"We'll come back next year," they said. "Back to this lovely land. We'll come back for another load of timber, and another load of grapes."

"We'll come back to the land of the grapes," Thyrker said.

And Leif said, "We'll come back to Vinland the Good."

So they sailed on across the ocean toward the east. And they left behind them the green forests, the fields where the grain was growing, and the hillsides with their fragrant grapes.

"The strange thing is that we never saw a single person there," one of the sailors said. "How could there be a land so beautiful, and not a single man was there until we came."

20.

THE RESCUE

THE galley was heavily loaded with its timber, so that the gunwales were low to the water line. But though the wind was brisk, the sea was not rough and they had no difficulty. Behind the ship the little boat with its grapes followed, and the odors of the new-cut logs, and the grapes, and the good salt wind, mingled together, spicy and exhilarating.

All the way across the ocean the men talked of Vinland the Good.

"We could go back as soon as the winter storms are over," one of them said. "We could go back to the same place we stayed before."

"But this time we could build solid houses, and stay right through the winter," another said. "We could bring sheep. They would find enough fodder there."

"And more tools," another said.

"Perhaps we could bring a whole fleet of galleys, with the women and children." It was the man who had expected his first baby speaking now. "Surely life would be much better for them there, after we had got the settlement started, than it would ever be in Greenland."

Leif thought, "My father was the one that brought the colonists to Greenland. Hundreds of them came from Iceland and Norway, so that a big community was started there in only a few years. Maybe I could do the same thing for Vinland. Vinland would be a better place to colonize. . . ."

So they sailed on under the fair wind, with the sun bright on them through the daylight hours, and the stars shining down at night. Leif steered a steady course northeast, for he calculated that this would be the shortest route back to Eriksfjord in Greenland.

One morning, after they had sailed thus, uneventfully, for nine days and nights, one of the sailors noticed that Leif was heading up sharply into the wind, and that his eyes were fixed on a point off the starboard bow. The sailor looked in the same direction, straining his eyes, but he could see nothing but the moving waves and the far horizon.

"Why do you head so sharp into the wind?" the sailor asked. "Would we not make better time if we kept a course before the wind?"

Leif did not answer his question. He kept his eyes fixed on the far horizon, and did not change his course. At length he said, "What do you see on that rock?"

The sailor did not even see there was a rock. They kept on in the same direction.

In an hour or so it was evident to them all that there was a rock, and that there was something moving on it. As they came closer it was plain that the rock was a small one, perhaps twenty feet across. Nothing was growing on it, not a tree or a bush, but the waves were throwing themselves up against it and breaking across it with white showers of spray. And as they came closer still, they saw that someone was standing and waving at them, and then they saw another lying on the stone.

Leif steered the vessel straight toward the rock, and soon they saw that the standing figure was that of a woman, and that an old man was lying at her feet.

"Lower a boat," Leif ordered when they had come close to the reef. "Bring them aboard the galley."

It did not take long to make the rescue. The girl, for she was not much more than a girl, helped them lift the old man who was her father aboard the skiff. They rowed back to the galley and brought them both aboard, and the old man was soon lying on the deck with a warm blanket over him. When they had forced a little ale between his lips his eyes opened, and he murmured what sounded like a word of thanks.

"He'll be all right now," Leif said to the girl.

"Take a little of the ale yourself. Here, put this blanket round you."

So the girl sat down with the blanket round her and began to sip the ale, and the color came into her cheeks, and Leif noticed that her hair was red.

"How did you come to be there?" he asked her, wondering that she could look so beautiful in a rough blanket.

The girl shivered. "I'm very cold," she said. "If you had an old tunic, I could put it on."

Leif started to his feet. "I should have thought of that," he said. "I'll bring you one of my own."

So he went below the deck, and soon he returned with a loose mantle of green velvet that he had worn at the court of King Olaf, and a long pair of leather leggings.

"Perhaps you could wear these," he said.

Then the girl, her name was Gudrid, went below and put on Leif's velvet mantle and his long leather leggings, and when she came back he saw that her hair was shining and smooth. She sat down beside her father.

"Eat this," Leif said, offering her a chunk of black bread and a piece of cheese. "You are hungry, aren't you?"

She looked at him gratefully, then broke the bread in two and handed it with a piece of the cheese to her father, who took it eagerly.

"We came from Iceland," she said. "My father was

a merchant there. He had a cargo of woolens to bring to Greenland, and he thought the trip would be an exciting one for me to take. . . . He did not know how it would turn out," she said, smiling gently as if to make excuses for him.

"We had a lovely galley," she continued. "One of the finest in Iceland. It was beautiful and most sea-worthy, and there were twenty oarsmen—" She put her head down on her arms, and Leif saw her shoulders moving and he heard her sobs.

They did not try to stop her tears. There on the deck of the galley the men sat in a great circle while the boat pushed its way across the water. The old man lay still on the deck, and the girl in the green velvet mantle cried.

At last she raised her head. "The Greenland Sea," she said, "we had been warned of it. We knew it was a treacherous place. We started across it, and the gale came up without any warning. It tore our sail into ribbons before we had a chance to lower it. Then the mast cracked, and shattered, and it fell on the deck where one of the men was standing. It struck his head, and he rolled, all bleeding, into the ocean. We could not get him. The waves were beginning to roll over our boat. It was all we could do to try to hang on.

"That was when my father tied me to a spar that had fallen on the ship. And he called to the crew to do the same thing. And he tied himself to another spar. And all the time the ship was plunging up and down, plunging up and down—" She shuddered. "Then someone cried out that the seams had sprung, and I saw the water pouring in. And then I was in the water, and the galley was gone. And all the crew were gone. There was not one of them there. But my father was in the water with me, and we were washing along with the waves. It was so cold, my hands and feet were numb, but I kept my head above the water. . . ."

"How long were you in the water?" Leif asked her.

"It seemed like ages," Gudrid said. "But it could not have been very long before we saw the little rocky island. We managed to swim over to it: the waves flung us up on the rocks . . . and we loosened the ropes that tied us to the spars. We stayed on that rock all night."

"In the morning," she continued, "when the storm was over, the wind subsided; the waves were beginning to go down. But the island was not more than twenty feet across—nothing but a heap of rocks in the sea. The sun came out and dried our clothes, and we got warm again. But there was nothing to eat or drink there: no sign of life of any kind anywhere on the horizon. For hours and hours we sat there, and wondered how long we could live. My father is an old man," she said, "and not very strong. The cold and the waves' buffetting were a terrible strain. And I had nothing I could give him to eat or drink. After a while, lying there, he lost consciousness—but I kept watching and watching. After a while I saw your ship—"

"And I saw you," Leif said. "From the very rim of the sea I saw you, when all the others said that there was nothing there." He moved a little closer to her, as if to confirm what his eyes had told him from so far away.

21.

LEIF THE LUCKY

THE sailors were in fine spirits. They could not stop talking about the rescue. Such a piece of luck it had been: but then they always knew that their commander was lucky. "Leif the Lucky" was what people would call him now. The name slipped from their tongues—"Leif the Lucky."

They agreed that they had all been lucky when it came to that. They might have rescued half-starved old sailors, who came from almost anywhere, and talked some language that they couldn't understand.

But here was Trygve, a gentle old man lying on the deck, mourning not because he had lost a valuable cargo, but because the men of his crew had died. "There were no finer men on the ocean," he kept telling them.

And here was Gudrid—Gudrid with her pink

cheeks and bright hair, Gudrid looking so slender in
the clothes that Leif had lent her. Gudrid came from
Iceland, a place that many of them knew well; and
she spoke their own tongue.

At first they were shy with Gudrid. What would
she think of them, they wondered. Would she find
them rough, uncouth? They had not been with women
for six months. They had not washed since they left
Vinland, and there only in the stream. Probably the
people Gudrid knew in Iceland took hot steam baths,
and were clean.

But that night when they sat together on the deck,
and the pot was boiling over its fire, they somehow
forgot their shyness. For Gudrid had learned their
names and liked to talk with them, and she herself
took up the ladle and ladled the stew into each man's
trencher as he held it out.

Leif watched them as they sat in a circle on the
deck. The men were right, he thought. He had been
lucky, perhaps more lucky than he knew.

"I'll take the helm tonight," Leif said to his steers-
man later. "Somehow I do not want to sleep."

So the men rolled themselves up in their fur blankets and lay on the deck, and Thyrker and the priest
lay with them. There was no sound save the wash of
the waves along the gunwales. And Trygve slept too,
a peaceful sleep after all his trials.

And Leif kept his eyes steady on the North Star
to hold the vessel on its course. But Gudrid, being

wakeful too, sat on the edge of the gunwale and
watched him.

On and on the vessel plunged through the waves
toward Greenland. And the men on the deck slept, and
the dark was round them. Only the iron lantern that
hung over the water at the stern of the boat went
swinging its little light on the foaming wake.

After a while Gudrid spoke. "Shall you be glad to
get back to Greenland?" she asked.

Leif considered. "Yes," he said. "I'll be glad to see
the glaciers sliding down the mountains, and the ice
floes drifting out to sea. It's a rough place, but I
like it."

"Shall you stay there always?" Gudrid asked.

Leif laughed. "A viking does not stay anywhere
always," he answered. "For the sea is a roadway that
leads all round the world, and the vikings follow it.
Some day I'll go trading in England, and Ireland.
Some day I'll go sailing up across the ocean at the
very top of the world, and then my ship will be on
the warm southern waters off Greece and Crete. A
viking doesn't stay anywhere."

"Shall you go back to Vinland?" Gudrid asked.

"That's it," Leif answered, a new warmth in his
voice. "As soon as I've traded and got rich enough,
I'll buy a whole fleet of galleys—the finest ships
afloat. I'll load them down with cattle and grain and
tools, and I'll persuade the strongest and most am-
bitious people in Greenland to come with me. We'll

start for Vinland again—back to that place where
the forest trees grow down to the edge of the water,
and the bright fish swim thick in the rivers, and the
birds are on every tree. We'll go back to the place
where the wild wheat grows, and the grapevines cover
the hillsides. Vinland the Good will be our new country. You do not know how soft and sweet smelling
the winds are there all through the summer, nor how
long the daylight lasts in summer—the days are
longer than the nights."

Gudrid said nothing. There was a long silence,
while the vessel rushed forward through the dark,
and the waves splashed softly against the side of the
boat.

At length Leif said, "And you—what will you do?"

"I do not know," Gudrid answered softly. "My
father lost his fortune when our ship was wrecked.
And he is an old man now. It will be hard for him to
get another. But I suppose we will go back to Iceland. . . . That's where we belong." Her voice trailed
off into the silence again.

He made no answer. The night and the silence were
around them; the stars were blazing over them; the
waves lapped along the side of the boat. Leif held the
tiller, and the wind filled the sail. The ship pushed
through the waves toward Greenland.

On the deck the crew were sleeping. But Leif and
Gudrid were awake, and though they did not talk,
they were conscious of each other's presence.

It was almost morning when they spoke again. The light was beginning to break across the ocean. And Leif was still holding the tiller: Gudrid was still sitting on her place on the gunwale of the boat.

Then Leif said, "Why can't you stay with me in Greenland, and be there when I come back from far voyaging, and go with me to Vinland, when I return there again?"

When he spoke it seemed to him as if he had made a great discovery, for it seemed as if he had seen Gudrid, who was to be his wife, for the first time.

She rose from her place on the gunwale then, and came over and sat beside him. His right hand was steady on the tiller, and the ship did not deviate from its course. But with his left arm he held her close, and when she put up her face, he kissed her on the mouth.

So when the morning came, lighting the tips of the little waves until they sparkled, Leif and Gudrid were close together. And when the sun rose warm and bright over the ocean, they sat close together still. Only when the sleeping men on the deck stirred and began to wake did they let each other go.

22.

THE HOMECOMING

THERE'S Greenland!" Leif said two days later. "There, off the starboard bow! See? There where you can see that dark line along the horizon with the white of the glaciers at the top? You'll see in a minute."

Gudrid strained her eyes. "Yes, I can see," she said.

"I'm going to try to head straight for Eriksfjord," Leif said, excitement in his voice. "You'll see the head-land where I used to stand and look out to sea, and the harbor where all the ships are tied. And back on the hill you'll see my father's house. That's where we'll go. My mother will look after you until the days of our betrothal are over. Then we'll marry, and you'll be mistress of a house of your own, with a big bunch of keys hanging from your belt." She smiled at the mention of the keys. They would be a symbol of her importance.

"You'll be the mistress of a house of your own, right there at Brattalid—right on my father's place."

Gudrid strained to see the shore, wondering what it would be like.

"My father cannot give me a dowry," she said after a while. "He cannot even give me a wedding feast. . . ."

"What does it matter," Leif said, smiling at her. "We'll be as surely married without a dowry as with one. And the feast doesn't make any difference at all."

"I don't believe it does," Gudrid answered.

Not long after that the galley landed with a fine show of polished shields lined along the gunwales, and the yellow sail shining in the sun. Then the news of their journey and the land that they had found was carried from man to man, and people came crowding down to the shore to see the cargo of timber and to wonder at the load of grapes.

And after that the sailors went ashore to join their families and friends whom they had not seen for so long, the slaves began unloading the cargo, and Leif took Gudrid and her father to his home in Brattalid, walking up the same rocky path that he had run along when he was a boy.

Erik stood outside the door of his house as Leif approached. When he saw that his son was not alone, but that an old man was with him, and a young girl, he called his wife.

"Come, Thorhild," he called. "Come quickly. Leif is back. He's bringing people with him."

Thorhild was beside him in a moment. "O Leif!" she cried. And she looked and saw him walking up the path, and saw the girl, and the old man that walked with him.

Then because women are granted a certain perception that men do not often have, she knew without being told that this was to be Leif's wife. And she took her in her arms, and kissed her.

They talked late into the night before the fire. Now and again Erik ordered more ale to be brought, now and again one of the slaves carried in fresh wood and threw it on the fire, but the talk went on.

They wanted to hear about the King of Norway: had he treated Leif cordially? Had the things he had to sell brought good prices? How long had he invited Leif to stay? And where had he gone then? No one had expected him to stay away so long on his first voyage.

So Leif told them of his sailing across the ocean, and of the new land he had found.

"A new land?" Erik kept inquiring. "Where is this land? What is it like?"

"It's a green land," Leif kept repeating. "A green land in the western sea. There's more timber there than you could cut in ten years—much more than ten years. I do not know how far the forests stretch. The air is milder than in Greenland. There's a kind of sweet smell in the air, maybe it comes from the grapes, I do not know."

Erik was fascinated. "A new land," he kept repeating. And then he said, "What kind of people does this land belong to. Did you have to fight them?"

Leif said, "We did not see a single person there. We stayed all summer and explored up and down the coast, and we saw deer and foxes and other furred animals, and there were fish and birds aplenty, but we did not see a single person. I can hardly believe it myself, in a place like that. . .

"After we had stayed in that land all summer, we loaded our galley with its cargo, and sailed back across the ocean—and we were lucky on that journey home—" Leif looked over to the place where Gudrid sat on a stool before the fire.

Then Trygve began to speak. He spoke slowly and sadly, telling of the terrible storm, of the rising waters of the Greenland Sea, of his ship's sinking. "All those good men, lost in the Greenland Sea," he said. "Thor had no pity on them." His head bent down. His thin beard lay on his chest. His right hand, which held his drinking horn, shook a little, so that the ale spilled.

"In Norway I heard of a new God," Leif said. "King Olaf Tryggvason believes in Him and King Olaf sent one of his priests here with me. It's said this God can save, where all the others fail. He is the Christ: his symbol is the cross—"

Erik swallowed the last of his ale, and put his drinking horn down on the table. "Let's have no talk of new gods," he said, angrily. "It is Thor who has been

with me all my life. Odin, and Freya, Frig and Baldur—those are gods that have been with our people
since the beginning. Why should we talk of change,
as if we wanted to cast off our old shoes, and put on
new ones." He grew more and more angry as he
spoke: the deep color mounted to his cheeks.

"When I was in England," he said, "I saw the
priests of that new God. They murdered our men,
and tried to set fire to our ships. Ask any viking who
goes to trade in the British Isles what he thinks of the
Christians—I will not have them talked of here."

"But the priest has come," Leif said. "He came on
my ship: Thyrker has taken him home with him. King
Olaf Trygvasson sent him to try to Christianize all
the people of Greenland."

"Let me lay my hands on him," Erik said.

Thorhild interrupted them. "We'd better sleep,"
she said. "We have talked almost all night. Later
we'll send word to the neighbors to come, and Leif and
Gudrid shall join hands in their betrothal. Then in
the spring we'll have the wedding. We shall have
much to do before the wedding day."

23.

THE MARRIAGE

LEIF rode to his wedding that spring day on a small black horse. He felt the sun warm on his corselet and his metal helmet, and there was a kind of softness in the air, even in Greenland. His father and his brothers were with him, and the men of his crew, and Thyrker, and some of his neighbors. They rode two by two along the rocky road that led from his father's house.

Leif and Gudrid had lived at Erik's house all through the winter while their own house was being built. Their house was to be a large one with a great feast hall, as befitted Erik's heir. And although the new house was only a little more than a mile from Erik's place, it was planned that the wedding should follow the Norse custom, Gudrid riding with some chosen women to the appointed place about a quarter

of a mile from the new home, and Leif coming to join
them with his cavalcade. Leif's mother had been most
insistent that the traditional customs should be followed. Erik had said it did not matter so long as the
marriage was sealed with the stroke of Thor's hammer.

So Leif and his cavalcade rode toward the appointed place that morning, and when they had come
to a turn in the road, they looked down upon the
grassy plain. There in the sun they saw the tents that
had been erected for the guests, the pennants flutter-
ing in the sunny air, and a confusion of people moving back and forth. Then Leif put spurs to his horse,
the others followed him, and they went racing with
clattering hoofs to the open space in the center of the
field.

There Leif jumped from the saddle, and stood for
a moment in the sun. His helmet had been burnished
till it glistened. The coat of mail was shining too, and
over it a mantle of deep blue velvet was thrown back
from the shoulders so that the bracelets of silver on
his bare arms shone in the light. The people moving
in and out of the tents heard Leif come and drew near
in a silent circle.

Then from the nearest tent, the curtain was drawn
aside and Gudrid moved toward Leif. Gudrid was
poor, but today she looked as a queen would look.
Her kirtle of softest yellow silk was belted at the waist
with a girdle of rich embroidery set thick with jewels.
The ends of her long red hair, smoothly brushed, were

tucked into the girdle. And around her head she wore
a long piece of thin filmy linen, like a veil. The veil
was wrapped around so that it covered her face, but
the long ends hung down behind, and were held by
two girls who were her bridesmaids.

Slowly, while no one spoke, Gudrid approached
Leif. And when she had come close he leaned down
and pulled aside the veil so that he could see the
familiar face, the blue eyes, the lips that smiled at him.

Then while the people waited, the black-robed
priest stepped toward them and began to murmur
the words that would make them man and wife. For
though Erik had objected, Leif and Gudrid had in-
sisted that they would be married by the Christian
priest. And when the priest had finished, Erik, who
stood beside his son, raised a great hammer in the air.
"Protect them, Thor," he cried. And when he raised
the hammer he remembered the day, not very long
ago, when he had called upon Thor in Iceland, and
cried out the name of his son.

Today no thunder and lightning gave evidence that
Thor had heard. The sun shone on the wedding: there
was hardly a cloud in the sky.

The dancing began when the ceremony was over.
Leif took Gudrid in his arms and began to dance with
her. And one after another the others started to dance,
back and forth and in and out, singing as they danced
until all the field was filled with motion. Now and
again they paused for some refreshment, and then

they danced on again while the sun traveled across
the sky and sank behind the glacier-covered Greenland peaks.

When the shadows fell the torches were lighted.
And the people danced on in the shadowy field. But
Leif took Gudrid then and lifted her to his saddle.
Unnoticed, they rode away from the field, out along
the road that led toward their new house.

The moon had risen as they approached it. They
could see the white light on the thatch of the roof.
Neither of them spoke when they came to the door.
Leif tied his horse to a post, and together they walked
in through the door.

"I'll make a fire," he said. "The evening air is cool."
And Gudrid sat down, and took off the great bunch
of keys from her belt and put them down on the
table. . . .

The sun woke them early next morning. It came
in bright through the window, lighting every corner
of the hall. The fire had died on the hearth, the ashes
looked gray and cold in the morning light.

"There's an old custom," Gudrid said, half smiling,
as if she thought herself too modern to be concerned
with old customs. "There's an old custom that on their
first morning together, the bride should give her
husband a gift."

Leif smiled. "I like old customs," he said.

"I have not much to give," Gudrid went on. "For
when our ship was sunk, all that I had was lost. But

when I sat there on that rock, after I had been washed ashore by the waves, I leaned down and picked up a piece of gray stone. 'I'll keep this small bit of stone,' I said to myself. 'If ever I come to land again, I'll have it to remember this rock by. I'll know then that I have been lucky.' So I hid it in a fold of my dress, and I kept it there, and I have kept it there ever since. And now I'm giving it to you, to remember that we have been lucky."

Leif took the small gray stone in his hand and turned it over on his palm, and smiled. And then without speaking he put it carefully in the leather pouch that was attached to his belt.

"I like old customs too," he said. "I'd like to give you something rare and precious. Something that would be worthy for a king to give his queen. But I have this for you."

From the same purse into which he had put Gudrid's gift, he took out now a small white shell.

"When I was in that wondrous land, I woke one morning early, before any of the others were awake. The leaves were rustling on the trees, and the birds were singing. I walked down to the shore, and a soft mist was rising over the water. And I picked up a shell. 'This little shell,' I said, 'this will be for me to remember how beautiful this morning is in this new world.' I have carried it ever since. And I have never even showed it to anyone before."

Gudrid took the shell and hid it in a fold of her kirtle. And then he kissed her again.

24.

LEIF IS THE LORD
OF BRATTALID

IN ERIK'S dreary hall at Brattalid one evening
in the winter that followed, Thorhild sat on a low seat
near the doorway sewing a pair of shoes. As she sewed
she wept: the tears ran down her cheeks so that often
she stopped to wipe them away.

For in the center of the hall, lying inert on his great
shield lay Erik. And Erik was dressed in full armor,
with corselet and helmet, his sword belted around his
waist. But his face was gray in death, his eyes sunk
in their sockets, his red beard like a frazzled rope of
tow on his sunken chest.

"I could not stop the fight," Thorhild was thinking, as she had thought so often in Erik's lifetime.

She sewed a few more stitches, and looked across to

where he lay. "This was his last fight," she said softly. "I could not stop it. Erik hated all that had to do with Christianity, for he was loyal to the old gods. When Thorbrand said he too was turning Christian, he fought him. Now he is dead. The great hall is empty now. He will not walk through it again. He will not call for ale, or laugh—"

Thorhild put down her sewing. Erik, cradled in his shield, did not stir.

After a time the door was pushed open and Leif and Gudrid entered. Gudrid came quickly and sat down beside Thorhild, but Leif walked to the place where Erik lay and looked down at him. There was his father: the familiar face, the red beard neatly combed, the blue eyes closed in death. He seemed somehow smaller than Leif remembered him—small and shrunken, as he lay there on his shield.

"Father," Leif said. But Erik did not stir. Leif felt as if he was a stranger lying there.

He turned at last to where his mother sat. "Are the shoes ready?" he asked. And Thorhild held them out to him.

Then Leif took the shoes his mother had made, and carefully but firmly he bound them to his father's feet.

"Now with his *hel* shoes he will be able to walk into the other world," he said. And Thorhild was pleased to think that she had made the shoes, even though they would take her husband from her.

"Do the new Christian doctrines teach that the *hel* shoes should be put on?" she asked Leif timidly. But Leif said he did not know. He had not heard they were forbidden.

Outside the door two sledges harnessed with oxen were waiting. Leif called to the drivers to help him, and gently they lifted the shield on which Erik lay and carried it out through the door and placed it on the sledge. Then Leif and his mother and Gudrid climbed into the other sledge, and slowly they made their way down the familiar snowy road toward the harbor.

A group of men and women had gathered at the shore. They drew aside to let them pass. At the water's edge the sledges stopped again, and Leif and the other men lifted the shield on which his father lay, and carried it carefully and set it on the great galley. Now the torches were lighted on the galley's deck and a steady breeze, gentle but persistent, sent their flames trailing through the dark.

"Start the fire," Leif called to the slaves who waited below the deck. In a few minutes a thin plume of smoke rose from the bottom of the ship and the slaves ran up the ladder and jumped to the shore. Leif and the others who had been aboard the galley followed them.

At last the galley was untied: the great sail was already swelling. And those who were on the shore watched while the wind took the ship toward the sea.

Further and further out toward the ocean it moved with its lonely silent occupant, the serpent prow cutting the water, the broad sail swelling, and a long white wake trailing behind.

"He was a great sailor—Erik," someone said. "There was no other who could navigate the Greenland Sea so well."

And another said, "He was loyal to the old gods. He could not stand even a mention of Christianity. That was his undoing. He would fight any man who slighted Thor or Odin. That last time he fought was the end for him."

Thorhild said to Gudrid who stood beside her, "He was so good to me. Again and again, when he had been banished from one place or another, he would start again, and build another home, and he always said he built them all for me—"

But Leif did not listen to the talk. He stood still, his eyes on the slow-moving ship where his father lay. And he was thinking, "He was my father. Now we shall not see him again. We shall not see the flash of his weapons in a fight, nor wait for him to come home from far voyaging. We shall not hear the tread of his feet across the floor, nor hear him call to have his horn filled with ale. We shall not hear him cry to Thor for help, nor curse the new gods whom he hated so. . . . Now I shall be the lord of Brattalid. And all the galleys and the slaves, and all the herds and the flocks, and all the lands, shall be mine. And I will send my fleets to the far off places—

"And I too will grow old, and I too will be faithful to those who depend on me, and I too will worship my own God."

He turned to his mother and Gudrid. "Let us go home," he said. "Let us go home, to Brattalid."

They turned, and began to walk together up the rocky road toward his father's house.

They had not gone far when they paused and looked out toward the harbor. The galley on which Leif's father traveled had made good headway. It was already well out to sea. As they watched they saw a white puff of smoke that seemed for a moment to blot out the ship. And then the smoke subsided, and a bright flame went shooting up. The flame was followed by another and another, until all the ship was a glorious flaming splendor. And then the flames subsided, like a bright flower trodden by a heavy foot. The waves washed across the place where the ship had been. And they knew that Erik the Red had left them to themselves.

25.

A NEW FLEET SAILS FOR VINLAND

WHEN the weather had settled in the spring, and a steady wind set toward the west, Leif had six galleys fitted up to sail back to Vinland.

"We'll take women and children as well as men," he told Gudrid. "We'll get there early in the year, and when we have built a great house to live in, we'll start cutting timber and gathering grapes to send to Greenland. But some of us will stay in Vinland; it will be a new community. With herds and flocks, and all the fruits of that country, and the fish off the coast, and the animals that roam the woods, life will be easy and good."

Gudrid smiled. "We'll love the warm days," she said. "And the green of the trees. You've told me so much, I feel as if I knew it there as well as you do."

So the days were busy with preparations. And many offered to go back with Leif to Vinland. Thyrker was eager to return to the land of the grapes, and planned to send back wine to Germany. He could make it in big wooden troughs, and ship it in skin bags, he said.

Leif's brothers, grown men now, with families of their own, wanted to join the expedition, and his halfsister Freydis planned to go. In all, more than a hundred persons—men, women, and children—were ready to turn their backs on Greenland and try a new life in a new world.

So the days of preparation passed quickly, and finally everything was in readiness. Food and water and casks of ale were stored in the hold of each ship, to be used on the voyage. Tools and sacks of grain had been brought aboard for planting in the new fields: sheep and goats, protesting, had been driven through the shallow water and hauled into the boats. The sails were set, the ships were pulling at their anchors.

On the shore a crowd of people were waiting to wave farewell to the departing travelers. The Norwegian priest was among them. He had not chosen to go to Vinland, for since he knew that no people were there, he thought there would be no chance of making converts. Greenland was fast becoming Christianized by his labors and he felt that he could be more useful at home.

Leif was to sail in the first galley, a beautiful black ship with a bright striped sail. When the people were all ready they sent for him to take command.

"Are you ready, Gudrid?" he called when the messenger brought word for him to start.

Gudrid ran to join him, and they stood for a moment in the room that they knew so well.

"We've been happy here," Gudrid said. "But I am not sad at going. Let's hurry."

She started to the door before him, and had just reached the threshold when he saw her sway. With one hand on the lintel of the door he saw her pause for a moment, then she fell unconscious to the ground.

"Gudrid!" Leif cried, running to take her in his arms. When he lifted her, her head fell back, her face was white, her eyes closed, and her long shining hair falling down.

He carried her across the room and laid her gently on the couch.

"Run for the wise woman," he called to the messenger who was still at the house. "Tell her to come quickly. Your mistress is very sick."

All that night the wise woman worked over Gudrid. She was an old woman with strong hands and deep wrinkles in her brown face, and she had ministered to many sick. Leif knew that if anyone could help Gudrid now, she could.

The wise woman rubbed Gudrid's hands and feet, called for more blankets to put over her, forced a little medicine between her pale lips. And all the time Gudrid with her white face did not stir or open her eyes, and her red hair lay still on the pillow.

Gradually the news of Gudrid's illness was carried to the people at the shore, and they came and sat in a silent throng outside the door. After a time the wise woman began to sing, a low crooning song calling to Gudrid's spirit to come back. And when the people outside the door heard it they joined in the song, singing softly, over and over again, till all the air was filled with the pleading refrain. But still Gudrid lay quiet, and Leif, watching her, could hardly see that she breathed at all.

So it was all afternoon, and when night came Gudrid was the same. The moon rose and shone down, its white light on the anxious people. Inside the house a low lamp burned. And Gudrid lay still on the couch, and Leif waited, while the song rose and fell round them all.

Morning came finally, after the long night.

"She may live," the wise woman said. "She may not. I do not know."

Then Leif sent for his brothers. "The ships are ready," he said. "The people are waiting to go. You take them. I will stay here with Gudrid."

So the people turned, and boarded the galleys. And the little fleet was soon under way for the new world. But Leif and the wise woman stayed with Gudrid.

26.

THIRTY YEARS LATER

OUTSIDE the door of his great house at Brattalid, Leif Eriksson stood leaning on his sword. The
house was the one his father had built when Leif was
still a boy. Its timbers of Norway pine stood low and
sturdy on the hill above the water. The mountains with
their blue-white glaciers rose behind it, and the sea
gulls dipped and circled over the moving waters of the
bay.

"Nothing has changed," Leif mused—yet he himself had changed, for thirty years had passed. Leif's
hair and beard were white now, his cheeks deep-fur-
rowed, and his shoulders a little stooped.

"Nothing has changed," he thought again, looking
around him at the mountains and the harbor. And
then he knew that everything but these had changed.

Far out on the water of the harbor he saw the fleet

of thirty vessels that he had sent to Norway with a cargo of eiderdown and furs, returning home.

"They'll reach the shore in half an hour," he thought, estimating the force of the wind. "I hope they got good prices in the Norway market—"

He slipped the sword into the jeweled scabbard that hung at his side, and started down the path that led to the harbor. It did not seem long to him since he had seen his brothers go down that path to the vessels that would take them to Vinland. He had not wanted to go with them, for Gudrid had been so sick. Yet when they came back two years later, and told of how they had fought with a people whom they called *skraelings,* and of how they had quarreled with each other afterwards, Leif had not been able to hold back his anger. If he had gone he would have managed to make friends with the *skraelings.* He would not have tolerated quarreling among his own men.

If he had gone back to Vinland, would it have been different with him? Leif wondered. Gudrid was gone now. And his mother, a good Christian, was dead. And Thyrker too, his foster father whom he had loved so much, was dead. There was no one close to him now, for Gudrid had borne him no children.

He looked across the harbor toward the fleet that moved steadily across the water, and paused to count —they were all there. Steadily, in groups of five, they were beating in before the wind. There was nothing in the world more beautiful than a fleet of serpent vessels coming home after a successful voyage.

He paused and smiled. He used to think there was one thing more beautiful, he remembered. That was the sight of a fleet setting out to sea.

He remembered his first command: his mother running down to the water's edge and putting her hand on the ship's prow, the excitement of the leave-taking, and the dull uneventful voyage.

But then the voyage back from Norway, nothing had been dull about that trip. How the wind had taken their ship and driven it across the water, how the spray flew back from the bow. And the wind whistled in the rigging as they went plunging through the sea.

"We didn't know where we were going," he thought. "And we didn't care. Just to feel the ship plowing through the waves, just to feel the wind, and to let ourselves go. . . . And there was no argument among us on that voyage. The men said, 'We'll go with you. We're bound to reach some land after a while.'

"And then the land we reached at last! The white strip of beach in the sun, the trees just coming into leaf, the soft sweet air. . . . And Thyrker finding those grapes," he said. "And the timber—a whole cargo of timber, easy to get."

"I wonder if it would have been different if I had gone back to Vinland?" he thought. "I might have established a trade, bringing timber and grapes. But the markets to the north and east seemed to have a richer promise. Or at least it seemed that way to me. Maybe if I had had a son—"

The thought of a son made him pause again. "If we had had a son," he said softly. Then quietly, because wisdom comes with years, he knew that whether he had a son or whether he did not, made little difference, for other men had sons.

He looked across the water toward the west, and thought of Vinland the Good. It lay there, out of his sight, but green and fresh nevertheless, with its trees, and running streams, and the hillsides where the wild grapes grew, and the wild wheat.

"I shouldn't wonder if a great many would cross the ocean to that place in the years ahead," he said. "Even if there are no markets there, people will want to go—"

He had reached the harbor, and sat on an upturned boat to watch the ships unload.

"If they do go, I shall have been the first," he said.